Spring Flowers of the Lower Columbia Valley

BY CLARA CHAPMAN HILL

Illustrated by Mary Comber Miles

SEATTLE • University of Washington Press • 1958

Contents

Introduction

This book is designed for people who want to know the names of the spring flowers but who have not had a course in plant identification. It is hoped that it will be useful to nature lovers, hikers, Boy Scouts, Girl Scouts, Campfire Girls, and students in general. The flowers here described are those which are in blossom by the middle of June and which can be found growing along the roadsides, in the woods, and in waste places. Many of the plants included are native to the Northwest, some have escaped from cultivation, and others have been introduced and become naturalized. Trees are omitted. For these the reader is referred to the pamphlet, *Trees to Know in Oregon,* Extension Bulletin 697, Oregon State College Press, or *Trees of Washington,* Extension Bulletin 440, the State College of Washington.

The area from which plants were collected for this book is the city of Portland and the territory embracing Tigard, Oregon City, Gresham, St. Helens, and Hillsboro. However, the plants of this area are typical of much of the region west of the Cascades from northern California to British Columbia.

Some Necessary Information

The use of technical terms has been kept at a minimum, but it is essential that the reader learn the names of the flower parts.

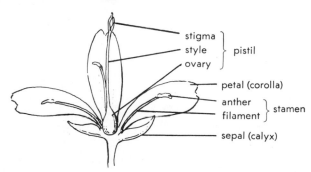

1. Flower parts

Sepals are the outer whorl of parts; they are usually green but they may be white or colored and petal-like. In some plants, such as skunk cabbage and dogwood, the conspicuous parts are bracts (modified leaves).

The ovary of the pistil contains the ovules, which after fertilization develop into seeds. As the seeds mature, the ovary wall also matures. This ovary wall plus its seeds constitutes the fruit of the plant, which may be dry as in peas and vetch or fleshy as in cherry or prune. When the ovary is located above the origin of the other flower parts, it is called superior. When it is located below the apparent origin of the other flower parts, it is said to be inferior.

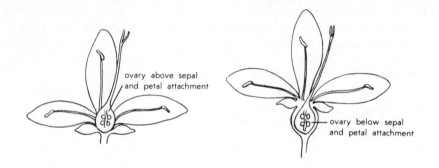

ovary above sepal and petal attachment

ovary below sepal and petal attachment

2. Superior ovary   3. Inferior ovary

Most flowers are the same all the way around and are called regular. Some, like peas and snapdragons, are bilaterally symmetrical, having a right and a left half, and are called irregular.

4. Regular flower   5. Irregular flower

Flowers may be borne singly (solitary) or in groups (an inflorescence).

 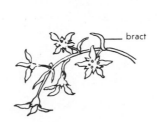 

6. Panicle   7. Raceme   8. Simple umbel

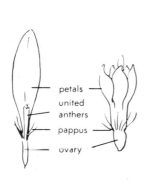  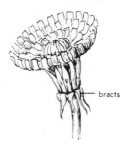

9. Compound umbel   10. Head of clover   11. Head of dandelion

12. Ray flower   13. Cyme
and disk flower (daisy)

Leaves differ in shape, margins, and degree of division.

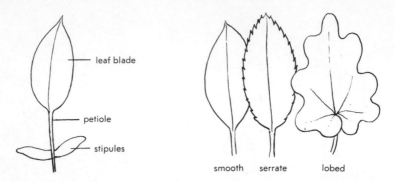

14. Leaf parts   15. Leaf margins

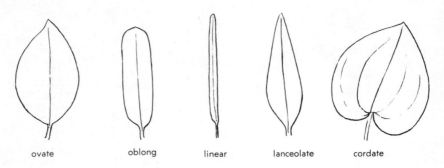

16. Leaf shapes

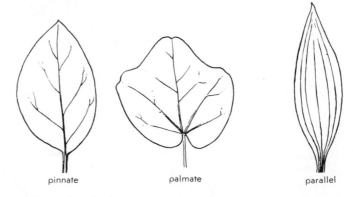

17. Venation

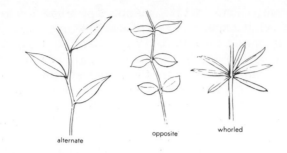

18. Leaf arrangement

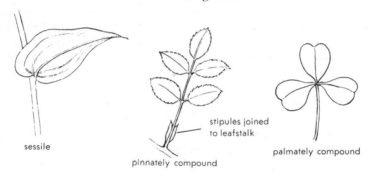

19. Sessile leaf (left); compound leaves (center and right)

Use of the Key

Many of the species described here are illustrated, making it possible to leaf through the pages and to identify a flower from a picture. However, if the beginner is interested in identifying plants, he will soon find it necessary to use a flora with few or no illustrations. Reference to a key is then the only means of identifying an unknown flower.

To use the key, compare the flower with the characteristics listed in the key. There is always a choice of two characteristics. Choose the one which best fits your flower, then read the next pair of characteristics listed below. Paired items bear the same number. Proceed in this fashion until the plant name is reached. Then find the name in the index and compare the plant with the description and the drawing, if it is illustrated. Refer frequently to the illustrations in the introduction and to the glossary, and be sure that each term used is understood.

Every plant has a two-part name, a generic name first and a

specific name second. All the members of a species are similar, and closely related species are grouped together into a genus. For example, all roses belong to the genus *Rosa*, but there are several different species of roses. Some are small weak plants like the wood rose, *Rosa gymnocarpa;* others, like sweetbrier, *Rosa rubiginosa,* are large and sturdy. Where there are many species in a single genus, as in the case of *Rosa*, there will be a second key on the page listed by the generic name. The letters following a specific name are an abbreviation of the name of the original describer of the plant. For a list of the abbreviations and the names for which they stand, see page 153. The complete name for sweetbrier is *Rosa rubiginosa* L. The letter L. stands for Linnaeus, the great Swedish botanist who first named and described the plant.

It is hoped that familiarity with this simple key will serve as an introduction to the use of the more complex keys found in the floras of larger areas.

Descriptions and Illustrations of Species

Each plant is described briefly and the range in which it may be found is given, after which any pertinent notes are added on the use of the plant, its edibility, or its distinguishing characteristics. Plant families are arranged in the order found in the plant floras of the Northwest, with the genera and species alphabetized. Family descriptions are given where more than one genus occurs in the family. All descriptions and drawings were made from fresh specimens which have been pressed and placed in the herbaria of Oregon State College and Portland State College.

The full-page illustrations are slightly less than natural size. Great care has been taken to use typical specimens for the drawings. However, it must be remembered that considerable variation exists within a single species.

20. Urn-shaped receptacle (rose)

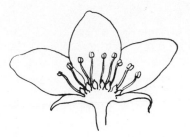

21. Enlarged receptacle (strawberry)

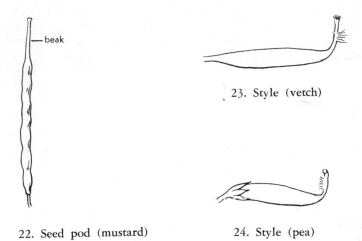

—beak

23. Style (vetch)

22. Seed pod (mustard)   24. Style (pea)

Spring Flowers of the Lower Columbia Valley

Key to Genera

1 Plants woody, shrubs or vines
  2 Flowers yellow
    3 Petals united into a tube; flowers surrounded by broad bracts and borne in pairs in leaf axils
                                       Bush honeysuckle, *Lonicera*
    3 Petals not united into a tube; flower bracts small or absent
      4 Leaves pinnately compound with 7 to 21 leathery, spiny leaflets; flowers regular
                                 Oregon grape, *Berberis*
      4 Leaves with 3 small leaflets; flowers irregular, pealike   Scotch broom, *Cytisus*
  2 Flowers not yellow
    5 Leaves compound with 3 or more separate leaflets (fig. 19)
      6 Flowers irregular, pealike; leaves very small, often missing   White-flowered broom, *Cytisus*
      6 Flowers regular, not pealike; leaves not small or missing
        7 Leaves opposite; flowers in showy, dense clusters
                              Elderberry, *Sambucus*
        7 Leaves alternate; flowers not as above
          8 Flowers greenish, minute, 1/4 inch or less across   Poison oak, *Rhus*
          8 Flowers not greenish, 1/2 inch or more across
            9 Pistils located within an urn-shaped receptacle (fig. 20); leaf stipules joined to the leaf stalk (fig. 19)   Rose, *Rosa*

3

9 Pistils on the surface of an enlarged receptacle (fig. 21); leaf stipules free from the leaf stalk

            Salmonberry, blackberry, *Rubus*

5 Leaves simple, not divided into separate leaflets

   10 Leaves opposite

     11 Woody vine; flowers orange

            Climbing honeysuckle, *Lonicera*

     11 Erect shrubs; flowers not orange

       12 Flowers dark red, borne 2 to 4 in the leaf axils

            Burning bush, *Euonymus*

       12 Flowers white, borne in terminal clusters

         13 Flowers large, 3/4 to 1 1/2 inches across, stamens many

            Mock orange, *Philadelphus*

         13 Flowers small, 1/3 inch across; stamens 4 or 5

           14 Leaf margins entire or wavy; twigs red to purplish red

            Creek dogwood, *Cornus*

           14 Leaf margins toothed; twigs grayish-brown

            Western wayfaring tree, *Viburnum*

   10 Leaves alternate

     15 Leaves palmately lobed (figs. 15, 17)

       16 Flowers red or greenish; sepals larger than the petals; stamens 5

            Currant, *Ribes*

       16 Flowers white; petals longer than the sepals; stamens many

         17 Flowers many, small, in terminal rounded clusters; bark shredding in strips

            Ninebark, *Physocarpus*

         17 Flowers 1 to 5, 1 inch or more across; bark not shredding

            Thimbleberry, *Rubus*

     15 Leaves not palmately lobed

       18 Flowers minute, in dense panicles (fig. 6)

         19 Leaves with 3 main veins from the base; flowers heavy-scented

            Buckbrush, *Ceanothus*

         19 Leaves with 1 main vein from the base; flowers not heavy-scented

            Ocean spray, *Holodiscus*

18 Flowers 1/4 inch or more across, not in panicles
  20 Petals united to form an urn or tube
    21 Twigs round, with a zigzag axis; ovary superior
                  Salal, *Gaultheria*
    21 Twigs angled or slightly ridged; ovary inferior
                  Huckleberry, *Vaccinium*
  20 Petals free from each other, not forming an urn or
      tube
    22 Pistils 5; pistillate flowers on one shrub, stami-
        nate flowers on another
                  Indian peach, *Osmaronia*
    22 Pistil 1; flowers perfect
      23 Flowers irregular, pealike; branches angled,
          often nearly leafless
                  White-flowered broom, *Cytisus*
      23 Flowers regular; branches rounded
        24 Stems with thorns; petals roundish in out-
            line   Hawthorn, *Crataegus*
        24 Stems without thorns; petals long and nar-
            row   Serviceberry, *Amelanchier*
1 Plants herbaceous, not woody
  25 Flowers borne directly on a fleshy spike surrounded by a
      broad yellow bract; leaves large, up to 3 feet in length
                  Skunk cabbage, *Lysichitum*
  25 Flowers not on a fleshy spike; leaves smaller
    26 Sepals and petals both absent; stamens many, white
                  Vanilla leaf, *Achlys*
    26 Sepals and petals both present, or petals absent
      27 Plants parasitic or saprophytic with no green color
          present; whole plant yellowish, flesh-colored, or
          purplish
        28 Flowers in a raceme, orchid-shaped; ovary in-
            ferior   Coralroot, *Corallorhiza*
        28 Flowers solitary or in a raceme, tubular; ova-
            ry superior Broomrape, *Orobanche*
      27 Plants not parasitic or saprophytic; green color
          present
        29 Flowers with the 3 outer segments spreading,
            the 3 inner segments larger and surrounding
            the 3-sided fruit; inner segments often with
            a corky protuberance
                  Dock, *Rumex*
        29 Flowers not as above

30 Sepals 3, petals 3, all the same color, or sepals green and
      petals white to purple
    31 Ovary located below the other flower parts (fig. 3)
        32 Flowers regular (fig. 4); leaves grasslike
            33 Sepals and petals unlike in shape; styles petal-
                like   Flag, *Iris*
            33 Sepals and petals alike in shape; styles slender
                                            Blue-eyed grass, *Sisyrinchium*
        32 Flowers irregular (fig. 5); leaves broad, not grass-
            like   Angel slipper, *Calypso*
    31 Ovary located above the origin of the other flower parts
      (fig. 2)
        34 Sepals 3, green; petals 3, white to purple
                                            Trillium, *Trillium*
        34 Sepals and petals the same color
            35 Leaves all basal
                36 Flowers bluish purple; leaves many, long and
                    narrow   Camass, *Camassia*
                36 Flowers cream-colored; leaves 2, mottled,
                    broad   Fawn lily, *Erythronium*
            35 Leaves alternate, opposite or whorled on the
                stem
                37 Stems unbranched; flowers borne at the end
                    of the stem
                    38 Flowers white; leaves alternate
                                    Solomon's-seal, *Smilacina*
                    38 Flowers reddish brown; leaves generally
                        whorled near the flowers
                                    Riceroot lily, *Fritillaria*
                37 Stems branched; flowers borne in leaf axils
                    or at the ends of branches
                    39 Flowers axillary, the flower stem bent or
                        twisted at the middle
                                    Twisted-stalk, *Streptopus*
                    39 Flowers at the ends of branches, the flow-
                        er stem not twisted
                                    Fairy bell, fairy lantern, *Disporum*
30 Sepals and petals not in threes; or sepals 3, petals absent
    40 Sepals 3, petals absent; leaves broadly heart-shaped
                                    Wild ginger, *Asarum*
    40 Sepals and petals not as above; leaves mostly not heart-
        shaped

41 Flowers in heads or headlike spikes or cymes (figs. 10, 11)
  42 Leaves opposite, stems angled
                       Corn salad, *Valerianella*
  42 Leaves alternate or basal; stems not conspicuously angled
    43 Individual flowers pealike; leaves with 3 leaflets
                  Clover, *Trifolium*
    43 Individual flowers either strap-shaped or tubular; leaves not with 3 leaflets
      44 Flowers trumpet-shaped, each with a bract at the base; stamens unequal in length
                  Collomia, *Collomia*
      44 Flowers not as above; stamens equal in length
        45 Heads daisylike with white or pinkish ray flowers and yellow tubular flowers (fig. 12)
          46 Leaves all basal, not lobed; plants small
                European daisy, *Bellis*
          46 Leaves not all basal, lobed or finely dissected; plants generally 1/2 foot or more tall
            47 Leaves finely dissected; plants much-branched
            Dog fennel, corn chamomile, *Anthemis*
            47 Leaves lobed; plants little-branched
                Marguerite, *Chrysanthemum*
        45 Heads not daisylike
          48 Heads many, in flat or dome-shaped clusters
            49 Leaves all alike, finely dissected; flower heads flattened
                Yarrow, *Achillea*
            49 Leaves of the stem bractlike, basal leaves large, palmately lobed, appearing after the flowers; flower heads cylindrical
                Sweet coltsfoot, *Petasites*
         48 Heads fewer or solitary, not in flat or dome-shaped clusters
          50 Flowers all strap-shaped
            51 Leaves in a basal rosette
              52 Green bracts at the base of the head in 2 layers, the outer bracts turned downward, the

inner erect; flowers stems hollow, without
bracts   Dandelion, *Taraxacum*
52 Green bracts at the base of the head all erect;
flower stems solid or with small green bracts
53 Flower-bearing stems branched; bearing
small bracts
False dandelion, *Hypochaeris*
53 Flower-bearing stems not branched, bearing
hairs but no bracts
Hawkbit, *Leontodon*
51 Leaves on the stem   Salsify, *Tragopogon*
50 Flowers all tubular
54 Marginal flowers larger; flowers not yellow
Bachelor's-button, *Centaurea*
54 Marginal flowers not larger; flowers all yellow
55 Bracts at the base of the head black-tipped,
heads cylindrical
Groundsel, *Senecio*
55 Bracts at the base of the head not black-tipped,
heads dome-shaped
Pineapple weed, *Matricaria*
41 Flowers not in heads or headlike spikes or cymes; sometimes densely clustered
56 Flowers very irregular (having a definite right and left
half)
57 Pistils 3; stamens many
Larkspur, *Delphinium*
57 Pistil 1; stamens 10 or fewer
58 Stamens 10, united around the pistil; flowers
pealike
59 Leaves palmately compound
Lupine, *Lupinus*
59 Leaves pinnately compound
60 Style of the pistil ending in a tuft of hairs
(fig. 23) Vetch, *Vicia*
60 Style of the pistil flattened below the stigma and hairy on the inner surface (fig.
24)   Pea, *Lathyrus*
58 Stamens 4 to 6; flowers not pealike
61 Petals free from each other
Violet, *Viola*
61 Petals united either at the tip or at the base
62 Leaves compound, arising from an under-

ground stem; petals 4; sepals 2

63 Flowers heart-shaped, drooping
Bleeding heart, *Dicentra*

63 Flowers spurred, the spurs all pointing in the same
direction Corydalis, *Corydalis*

62 Leaves simple, opposite; petals 5, united; sepals 5

64 Stems 4-angled; ovary 4-lobed

65 Leaves kidney-shaped, green; flowers solitary in
the leaf axils Creeping Charlie, *Glecoma*

65 Leaves ovate, usually purplish; flowers whorled
in the upper leaf axils
Dead nettle, *Lamium*

64 Stems not 4-angled; ovary not 4-lobed

66 Flowers yellow, with purplish dots
Monkey flower, *Mimulus*

66 Flowers blue or red

67 Flowers reddish, in a spreading inflorescence; plants large, 2 to 6 feet tall
Figwort, *Scrophularia*

67 Flowers blue, opposite or whorled in the
upper leaf axils; plants mostly under 1 foot
tall Blue-eyed Mary, *Collinsia*

56 Flowers regular (the same all the way around), or only
slightly irregular

68 Leaves whorled, opposite, or united about the stem

69 Stem leaves whorled or appearing so

70 Stem leaves in a single whorl beneath the flower
or flowers

71 Leaves 3; flower parts all free
Windflower, *Anemone*

71 Leaves 3 to 6; petals united at the base
Starflower, *Trientalis*

70 Stem leaves in several whorls

72 Plants branching from the base; stems not
square; leaves threadlike
Corn spurry, *Spergula*

72 Plants not branching from the base; stems
square; leaves linear or oblong, not threadlike Bedstraw, *Galium*

69 Stem leaves opposite or united around the stem

73 Flowers greenish, in drooping axillary clusters;
plants with stinging hairs
Nettle, *Urtica*

73 Flowers white, pink, red, or blue, not drooping; plants
   without stinging hairs
   74 Petals united into a tube; main stem prostrate, flower-
   bearing stem erect
      75 Flowers pink, bell-shaped, borne in pairs on erect
   flower stalks   Twinflower, *Linnaea*
      75 Flowers blue, not in pairs, borne close to the leaves
   Periwinkle, *Vinca*
   74 Petals free or only slightly joined at the base; main stem
   erect, some weakly so
      76 Sepals 2, basal leaves and stem leaves different
   Candy flower, miner's lettuce, *Montia*
      76 Sepals 4 or 5; basal and stem leaves alike
         77 Petals partly united (all pull off together)
            78 Stamens 2; petals 4; calyx 4-lobed
   Speedwell, *Veronica*
            78 Stamens 5; petals 5; calyx 5-lobed
               79 Stamens opposite the petals; flowers or-
   ange to scarlet; calyx without append-
   ages   Pimpernel, *Anagallis*
               79 Stamens alternate with the petals; flow-
   ers white or bluish; calyx with small
   backward-turned appendages
   Nemophila, *Nemophila*
         77 Petals free from each other
            80 Stamens and pistils on separate plants; flow-
   ers 1 to 1 1/2 inches long
   White campion, *Lychnis*
            80 Stamens and pistils in the same flower; flow-
   ers much smaller
               81 Leaves simple, entire
                  82 Petals notched or deeply cut; leaves
   ovate
                     83 Petals notched; plants hairy
   throughout
   Mouse-ear chickweed, *Cerastium*
                     83 Petals deeply cut into 2 parts;
   plants with a line of hairs down
   one side of the stem
   Chickweed, *Stellaria*
                  82 Petals not notched or cut; leaves
   narrow

84 Plants erect; flowers white; leaves without stip-
    ules   Sandwort, *Arenaria*
84 Plants prostrate, forming mats; flowers pink or red;
    leaves with papery stipules
                        Pink sand spurry, *Spergularia*
81 Leaves compound or lobed
    85 Leaves palmately lobed or parted
                        Geranium, *Geranium*
    85 Leaves pinnately divided into fine segments
                        Filaree, *Erodium*
68 Leaves alternate on the stem or at the base of the plant, of-
    ten forming a rosette
    86 Leaves conspicuously parallel-ribbed (fig. 17)
        87 Leaves all basal; flowers brown, papery, in an elon-
            gated spike   Plantain, *Plantago*
        87 Leaves 2 or 3 on the stem; sepals and petals white;
            flowers in a raceme
                        Wild lily of the valley, *Maianthemum*
    86 Leaves not conspicuously parallel-ribbed
        88 Sepals 4; petals 4; stamens 6, 4 long and 2 short
            (rarely only 4)
            89 Seed pod less than 4 times as long as wide
                90 Leaves all, or mostly, basal; flowers white,
                    minute
                    91 Fruit notched at the apex; stems with a
                        few clasping leaves
                                Shepherd's purse, *Capsella*
                    91 Fruit oval, flat; leaves all basal
                                Whitlow grass, *Draba*
                90 Leaves on the stem; flowers purple to white;
                    mature pod large, round or oval; stems and
                    leaves long-hairy
                                Honesty, *Lunaria*
            89 Seed pod more than 4 times as long as wide
                92 Pod not splitting to discharge seeds, filled
                    with a pithy substance; petals with distinct,
                    conspicuous veins
                                Radish, *Raphanus*
                92 Pod splitting to discharge seeds, not pithy in-
                    side; petals not conspicuously veined
                    93 Flowers yellow or orange

94 Flowers orange; leaves narrow
Wallflower, *Erysimum*
94 Flowers yellow; leaves not narrow
95 Seed pod with a definite beak beyond the seeds
(fig. 22)   Mustard, *Brassica*
95 Seed pod without a definite beak
96 Leaves clasping at the base; flowers 1/4 inch
long; stigmas not 2-lobed
Winter cress, *Barbarea*
96 Leaves not clasping at the base; flowers minute; stigmas distinctly 2-lobed
Hedge mustard, *Sisymbrium*
93 Flowers white, pinkish, or lavender
97 Flowers fragrant; pods much constricted between the
seeds   Rocket, *Hesperis*
97 Flowers not fragrant; pods not constricted between
the seeds
98 Flowers pink to lavender; stem leaves near the
inflorescence   Spring beauty, *Dentaria*
98 Flowers white; leaves in a basal rosette or leafy
all along the stem
99 Stem leaves clasping, simple
Tower mustard, rock cress, *Arabis*
99 Stem leaves not clasping; leaves compound
Bitter cress, *Cardamine*
88 Flowers not with 4 sepals, 4 petals, and 6 stamens
100 Main stem trailing or climbing
101 Plants with tendrils; flowers white, in racemes
Wild cucumber, *Echinocystis*
101 Plants without tendrils; flowers purple, in an angular inflorescence
Nightshade, *Solanum*
100 Main stem erect, not trailing or climbing (runners
present in strawberry and sedum)
102 Flowers borne in umbels (figs. 8, 9)
103 Flowers purple, in headlike umbels
Purple snakeroot, *Sanicula*
103 Flowers white; umbels not headlike
104 Bracts at base of the umbel pinnately
divided
Wild carrot, *Daucus*
104 Bracts at base of the umbel absent or
narrow, entire

105 Umbels with 10 to 30 rays; plants 3 to 10 feet tall
    106 Main stem with reddish spots; leaves finely di-
        vided   Poison hemlock, *Conium*
    106 Main stem green, ribbed; leaves divided into
        threes   Cow parsnip, *Heracleum*
105 Umbels with 3 to 8 rays, wide-spreading; plants un-
    der 2 feet tall   Sweet cicely, *Osmorhiza*
102 Flowers not borne in umbels
107 Stamens more than 10
    108 Stamens united by the filaments; leaves roundish,
        palmately cut into segments
                Wild hollyhock, *Sidalcea*
    108 Stamens not united; leaves not roundish in outline
        109 Petals with spurs; sepals petal-like, scarlet
            Columbine, *Aquilegia*
        109 Petals not spurred; sepals green or white
        (falling early in California poppy)
           110 Flowers in large, white, plumelike
              clusters; plants 3 to 6 feet tall
              Goatsbeard, *Aruncus*
           110 Flowers not in plumelike clusters;
              plants mostly under 3 feet tall
              111 Calyx 5-lobed; alternating with 5
                  bractlets
                  112 Leaves with 3 leaflets; flowers
                     white
                  Strawberry, *Fragaria*
                  112 Leaves pinnately compound at
                     the base of the plant; flow-
                     ers yellow
                  Large-leaved avens, *Geum*
              111 Calyx of 2 to 5 separate sepals,
                not alternating with bractlets
                113 Flowers greenish; petals ab-
                  sent; stamens and pistils on
                  separate plants
                Meadow rue, *Thalictrum*
              113 Flowers white, yellow, or or-
                  ange; stamens and pistils in
                  the same flower
                114 Flowers white; stamens
                  conspicuous, longer

than the petals and sepals
>Baneberry, *Actaea*

114 Flowers yellow to orange; stamens not as above
>115 Pistil 1; leaves finely divided
>>California poppy, *Eschscholtzia*

>115 Pistils many; leaves lobed or compound
>>Buttercup, *Ranunculus*

107 Stamens 10 or fewer
>116 Leaves compound with 3 leaflets
>>117 Leaflets with smooth margins, notched at the apex; flowers 1/2 to 1 inch across
>>>Wood sorrel, *Oxalis*

>>117 Leaflets lobed and toothed; flowers smaller
>>>Coolwort, *Tiarella*

>116 Leaves simple or, if compound, more than 3 leaflets present
>>118 Leaves with entire or toothed margins, not lobed or compound
>>>119 Stamens 10
>>>>120 Flowers yellow; leaves fleshy, smooth
>>>>>Stonecrop, *Sedum*

>>>>120 Flowers white; leaves not fleshy, often hairy Saxifrage, *Saxifraga*

>>>119 Stamens 5 or fewer
>>>>121 Petals turned backward exposing the united anthers
>>>>>Nightshade, *Solanum*

>>>>121 Petals not turned backward; anthers not united
>>>>>122 Petals with conspicuous crests at the center of the flower; inflorescence mostly 1-sided
>>>>>>123 Flowers white
>>>>>>>Scorpion grass, *Plagiobothrys*

>>>>>>123 Flowers pink, blue, or yellow
>>>>>>>124 Flowers in a loose panicle; plants stout
>>>>>>>>Western hound's-tongue, *Cynoglossum*

>>>>>>>124 Flowers in a coiled inflorescence; plants small
>>>>>>>>Forget-me-not, *Myosotis*

>>>>>122 Petals without crests; inflorescence not 1-sided

125 Sepals and petals 4; stamens 2
  126 Leaves all basal; flowers in racemes
                    Spring queen, *Synthyris*
  126 Leaves all along the stem; flowers solitary in the
      leaf axils   Speedwell, *Veronica*
125 Sepals 2; petals 5; stamens 3
                    Narrow-leaved montia, *Montia*
118 Leaves lobed or compound
  127 Sepals and petals free from each other
    128 Flowers white; sepals and petals bent sharply
      backward   Inside-out flower, *Vancouveria*
    128 Flowers magenta; petals not bent backward
                    Geranium, *Geranium*
  127 Sepals partly united into a cup; petals free or only
    slightly united
    129 Leaves pinnately parted or compound; petals
      partly united
      130 Stamens short; calyx with small, backward-
        turned appendages
                    Nemophila, *Nemophila*
      130 Stamens extending beyond the petals; calyx
        without appendages
                    Waterleaf, *Hydrophyllum*
    129 Leaves palmately lobed; petals free from each
      other
      131 Stamens 10; petals greenish white to pink
        132 Petals finely divided into fine segments;
          styles 2
                    Fringe cup, *Tellima*
        132 Petals deeply 3- or 5-lobed; styles 3
                    Starflower, *Lithophragma*
      131 Stamens 5 or fewer; petals white, brownish,
        or green
        133 Flowers in a wide-spreading panicle
                    Alumroot, *Heuchera*
        133 Flowers in racemes
          134 Calyx deeply cleft on the lower
            side; petals brownish, hairlike
                Youth-on-age, *Tolmiea*
          134 Calyx not cleft; petals greenish,
            fringed
                Bishop's-cap, *Mitella*

Plant Descriptions

ARUM FAMILY, Araceae

Skunk cabbage, *Lysichitum americanum* Hultén and St. John
  Leaves all basal, oblong, 12 to 36 inches long; flowers minute, green, borne on a fleshy stalk (spadix), surrounded by a yellow, leaflike sheath (spathe).
  Wet, swampy areas; west of the Cascades from Alaska to California and east to Idaho and northwestern Montana. Skunk cabbage is one of the first plants to blossom in early spring, the big spathes appearing before the leaves. When the leaves are bruised or crushed there is a skunklike odor, which accounts for the common name. The root is the chief ingredient of the patent medicine "Skookim," a stimulant, antispasmodic, emetic. The roots are said to have been an important item in the diet of the northwestern Indians, and were eaten in the spring when they were tender. Deer, bear, and elk eat the plant also, and bees gather the pollen. The big yellow spathes and handsome leaves make this an excellent addition to any bog garden.

LILY FAMILY, Liliaceae

  Herbs with rootstocks, bulbs, or corms; flower parts in threes (except lily of the valley); petals and sepals usually alike; ovary superior; fruit a capsule or berry.

Large camass or great camass, *Camassia leichtlinii* (Baker) Wats.
  Plants resembling small camass but stouter and taller; sepals

16

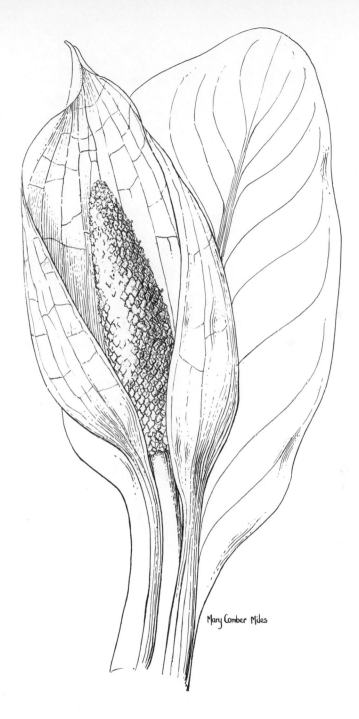

Skunk cabbage. *Lysichitum americanum*

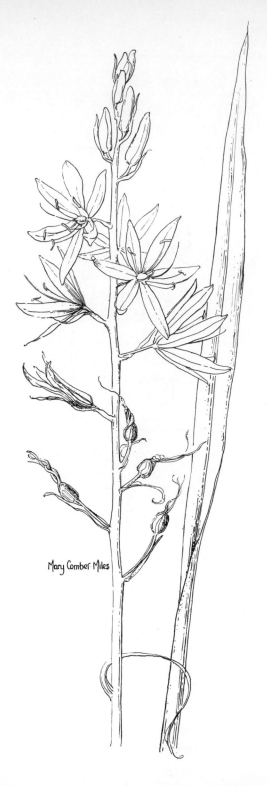

Large camass or great camass. *Camassia leichtlinii*

Fairy bell. *Disporum oreganum*

Mary Comber Miles

Fairy lantern. *Disporum smithii*

and petals evenly arranged, twisting together above the fruit with age.

Meadows; mostly west of the Cascades from Vancouver Island to California. This species is less common in the Portland area than small camass. It can be distinguished from small camass by its larger size, the even distribution of the sepals and petals, and the twisting together of the flower parts with age. Occasionally large camass has creamy white flowers.

Small camass or common camass, *Camassia quamash* (Pursh) Greene

Stems and leaves arising from an onionlike bulb; leaves all basal, narrow and grasslike; flowers showy, with both sepals and petals a dark purplish blue or sometimes light blue to white; sepals and petals not evenly arranged, each drying and twisting separately with age.

Fields and low mountains; west of the Cascades and east to Montana. Camass is found in areas which are very wet in spring and in winter and dry in the summer. It is an attractive hyacinthlike plant and makes excellent garden and cut flowers. Before the white man's cultivation of the Willamette Valley, the meadows were blue with camass. The bulbs constituted a major portion of the food of the western Indians and, later, of the early settlers. Collecting was usually done in late June after the blossoms and leaves had disappeared. The bulbs were stored, later to be roasted, boiled, fried, or pounded into flour. The annual root festival of the Warm Springs Indians takes place in April as a celebration of thanksgiving to the Great Spirit for bountiful yields from the forest, soil, and streams. Camass is one of the four roots prepared and eaten at this feast.

Fairy bell, *Disporum oreganum* (Wats.) B. and H.

Plants branching, 1 to 2 feet tall; leaves oval, heart-shaped at the base, long-pointed at the tip; flowers 2 to 5 in clusters at the apex of the branches; sepals and petals white or greenish, spreading, shorter than the stamens and pistil; stigma entire or only slightly branched into 3 parts.

Shaded woods; west of the Cascades from British Columbia south to the Siskiyou Mountains.

Fairy lantern, *Disporum smithii* (Hook.) Piper

Plants branching, usually 1 to 2 feet tall, occasionally reaching 3 1/2 feet; leaves oval in outline, heart-shaped or rounded at the

Mary Comber Miles

Fawn lily. *Erythronium oregonum*

base, long-tapering at the apex; flowers 2 to 5 in a cluster borne
at the apex of the branches; sepals and petals white or creamy,
extending beyond the stamens and pistil; stigma 3-branched.

Wooded areas; west of the Cascades from British Columbia to
California. The foliage of these two species is so much alike that
positive identification is difficult without the flowers. With flowers present, however, they can be distinguished by the spreading flower and protruding stamens in *D. oreganum* and the closed
flower and covered stamens in *D. smithii*. Also, the stigma is 3-
branched in *D. smithii,* and entire or only minutely branched in
D. oreganum.

Fawn lily, *Erythronium oregonum* Applegate
    Plants arising from a bulblike underground stem; leaves 2, mot-
tled, oblong, opposite each other at ground level; flower stem
arising between the leaves, bearing 1 to 6 cream-colored flowers;
sepals and petals alike, turned backward at the middle, deep yellow at the base; stamens with yellow anthers; stigma 3-branched.

Open woods; west of the Cascades in Washington and Oregon.
This is one of the most graceful of our early spring flowers. Although the bulbs are edible and were eaten by the Indians, the
beauty of the flower is such that the bulbs should not be destroyed.
Like *Crocus,* the bulbs may be naturalized in grass or planted in
clusters.

Other common names often used for this plant are: dogtooth
violet, adder's-tongue, lamb's-tongue, and trout lily.

Riceroot lily or mission bell, *Fritillaria lanceolata* Pursh
    Stem unbranched, 1 to nearly 3 feet tall, arising from a bulb
covered with small ricelike bulblets; leaves long and narrow, generally whorled; flowers nodding, 1 to 1 1/2 inches across, bell-
shaped, purplish, mottled with greenish yellow; petals and sepals
alike, each with a large dark gland below the middle; styles 3,
longer than the stamens.

Shaded areas; west of the Cascades from British Columbia east
to Idaho and south to California. This is one of the many bulbs eat-
en by the north-coast Indians. Leslie L. Haskin, who has cooked
and eaten many of our native plants, says in *Wild Flowers of the
Pacific Coast* (Portland, Ore., 1934) that the bulbs are tender and
delicate, differing little from genuine rice.

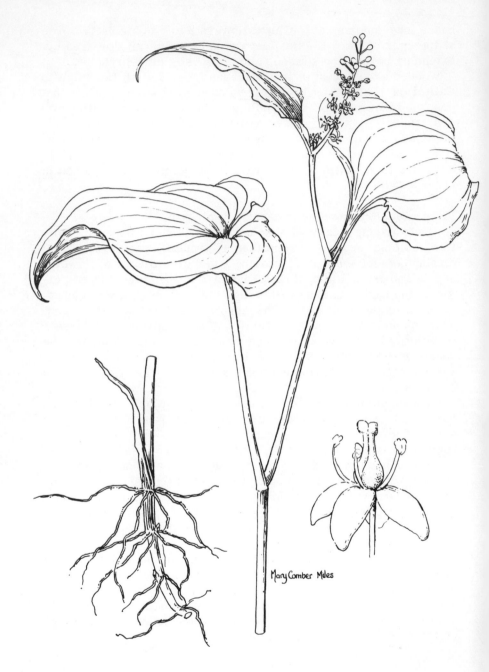

Wild lily of the valley. *Maianthemum bifolium*

Large false Solomon's-seal. *Smilacina racemosa*

Mary Comber·Miles

Small false Solomon's-seal. *Smilacina sessilifolia*

Wild lily of the valley, *Maianthemum bifolium* DC. var. *kam-tschaticum* (Gmel.) Jepson

Plants from a creeping rootstock; upright stem with a zigzag growth habit; leaves usually 2, heart-shaped at the base, acute at the apex, parallel-veined, the lower leaf with a longer leafstalk; a third smaller or much-reduced leaf often present just below the flower cluster; flowers small, 3/8 inch across, cream-colored; sepals 2; petals 2; stamens 4, opposite the sepals and petals.

Moist shady woods; from the Cascades to the Coast, and from Alaska and Idaho to California. This genus differs from others in the lily family in having the flower parts in twos and fours instead of in threes. The fruit is an edible red berry, and it has been used as food by the Indians. This plant is attractive in terrariums or shaded rock gardens.

Large false Solomon's-seal. *Smilacina racemosa* (L.) Desf.

Plants reaching 3 or more feet in height; leaves oblong, tapering to a pointed apex, without a leafstalk; flowers many, cream-colored, in a branching cluster.

Moist woods; from British Columbia to California and east to the Atlantic Coast.

Small false Solomon's-seal, *Smilacina sessilifolia* Nutt.

Plant up to 2 feet in height; leaves alternate, parallel-veined, tapering to a long point; leafstalk absent; flowers starlike, few, cream-colored, on a zigzag axis.

Moist, shady woods; British Columbia to California and east to Montana and Utah. Both the false Solomon's-seals have a creeping underground rootstock bearing the scars of old branches. These scars are said to resemble a seal made in wax. The true Solomon's-seals (*Polygonatum*) are found east of the Rocky Mountains. They resemble our plants but bear the flowers in the leaf axils all along the stem. Our two species can be easily distinguished by the many flowers in a plumelike cluster in *S. racemosa* and the few flowers in *S. sessilifolia*. Both are handsome plants, in blossom and again when the red berries mature, and they are excellent in shady garden plantings.

Twisted-stalk, *Streptopus amplexifolius* (L.) DC.

Stems branching, 1 to 3 feet tall; leaves alternate, clasping the stem, tapering at the apex; flowers white, hanging singly in the leaf axils, the stalk of each twisted in the middle; sepals and petals spreading or bent backward.

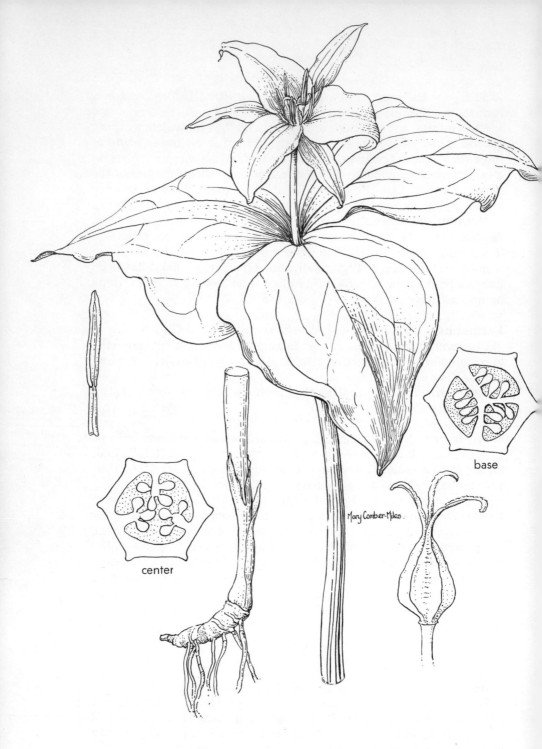

center

base

Mary Comber-Miles.

Trillium or wood lily. *Trillium ovatum*

Moist woods from the Pacific to the Atlantic, also in Europe and Asia. Twisted stalk, fairy lantern, and fairy bell are very similar in general appearance. The flowers in all are hidden by the leaves, and one must raise the branches and examine the flowers in order to identify the plant. Twisted-stalk can be distinguished by the kink in the flower stalk and by the fact that the flowers are borne singly in the leaf axils. The scarlet berries are eaten by some people and have been given the name scootberries because of their cathartic properties.

Trillium or wood lily, *Trillium ovatum* Pursh
Stem rising from a short, thick rootstock; leaves in a whorl below the flower, broadly ovate, pointed at the apex; flowers single, on a stalk above the leaves; sepals 3, green; petals white when young, turning lavender, then purple with age; stamens 6; style 3-branched.
Common in moist woods throughout the Northwest. This is perhaps the best known of our spring flowers. Its name, trillium, comes from the Latin prefix *tri*, meaning triple and is derived from the fact that it has 3 leaves, 3 sepals, 3 petals, twice 3 stamens and 3 stigmas.
Another species occasionally found near Portland is the sessile trillium, *Trillium chloropetalum* Howell. It differs in having the leaves mottled with spots of reddish brown and in having no flower stalk, the flower sitting directly at the center of the whorl of leaves. The petals of the sessile trillium are long and narrow and not as showy as those in *T. ovatum*.

IRIS FAMILY, Iridaceae

Herbs with grasslike, parallel-veined leaves; flowers 1 to several, usually showy; sepals and petals the same color; stamens 3; styles 3; ovary inferior.

Flag, *Iris tenax* Dougl.
Leaves mostly basal, grasslike; stem leaves few, alternate, clasping the stem; flowers single or in twos; sepals purple, spreading, larger than the petals, conspicuously veined with deep purple, yellow at the center; petals also purple, narrower than the sepals, erect; styles 3, petal-like and opposite the sepals; stamens 3, lying in the groove on the underside of the styles.
Open fields and hillsides in western Oregon. The usual color of the flower is purple but many variations occur from palest lav-

Flag. *Iris tenax*

ender to the deepest shades of purple. This is an excellent garden plant.

Blue-eyed grass, *Sisyrinchium sarmentosum* Suksd.
Stems flattened, 8 to 20 inches tall; leaves grasslike, shorter than the flower stem; bracts below the flowers unequal in length, one generally extending beyond the flowers; flowers blue or purplish with a yellow center; petals and sepals alike; ovary inferior; stigmas 3.
Wet meadows; British Columbia, Washington, Oregon, and Idaho. The flowers are short-lived, lasting only a day or part of a day.

ORCHID FAMILY, Orchidaceae

Herbs with irregular flowers; the 3 sepals and 2 of the petals alike, the third petal spurred or saclike; stamens and style united into a column; ovary inferior.

Angel slipper, *Calypso bulbosa* (L.) Oakes
Flower stalk 3 to 7 inches tall, arising from a bulblike underground stem lying just under the surface; the single leaf basal, broadly ovate, 1 1/2-3 1/2 inches long, often heart-shaped at the base; flower irregular, slipperlike, rose-purple, reaching 1 inch or more in length; stamens and style united into a broad petal-like column.
Dense moist woods; mostly west of the Cascades from Alaska to California. Found also from Labrador south to Maine, New York, and Michigan, and in Europe. This delicate little orchid is one of the most beautiful of our native flowers, but it is fast becoming rare. Because the bulb lies in the moss close to the ground surface, careless pickers pull up the bulb with the flower. This plant and the *Corallorhiza* species should not be gathered at all since they rarely survive in gardens.

Coralroot, *Corallorhiza*

The members of this genus are saprophytes, which means that they derive their food from decayed organic matter. The entire plant appears reddish and the leaves are reduced to sheathing scales.

Spotted coralroot, *Corallorhiza maculata* Raf.
Stem 8 to 20 inches tall, purplish; leaves 2 to 4, scalelike; flow-

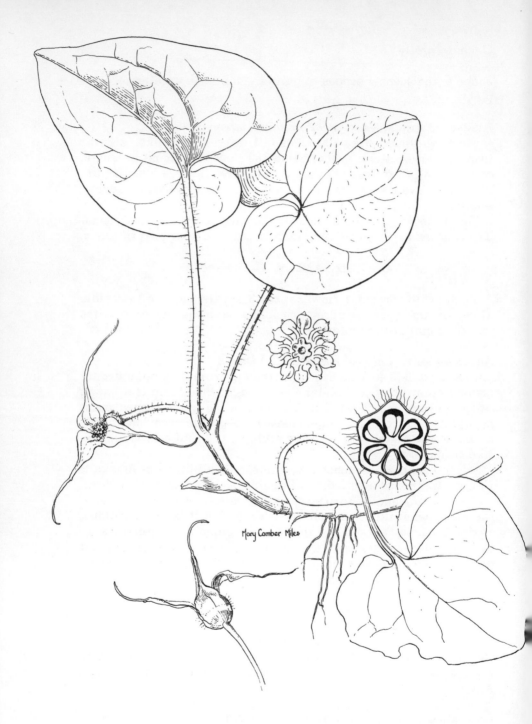

Wild ginger. *Asarum caudatum*

ers in a raceme, spurred; sepals and upper petals brownish purple; lower petal whitish, broad, 3-lobed, spotted with purple or red.

Deep coniferous woods; British Columbia south to California and east to the Atlantic Coast.

Striped coralroot, *Corallorhiza striata* Lindl.

Plants with no green color, arising from a branched, coral-like root; leaves scalelike, reddish; flowers in a raceme; sepals and upper petals flesh-colored, narrow, striped with dark red or purple; lower petal broad with 3 dark purple stripes.

Deep coniferous woods; British Columbia to Ontario, south to California and east to Wyoming, Michigan, and New York.

NETTLE FAMILY, Urticaceae

Nettle, *Urtica lyallii* Wats.

Perennial herb, 1 to 6 feet tall with stinging hairs on stem and leaves; stems angled; leaves opposite, ovate, rounded or cordate at the base, acuminate at the apex, coarsely toothed, veins prominent; stipules present; stamens and pistils in separate flowers on the same plant; flowers small, greenish, in dense axillary clusters; sepals 4; petals absent.

In woods and thickets; west of the Cascades from Alaska to Oregon and east to Idaho. In ancient medicine the nettle was used for urtication, a practice of whipping or stinging paralyzed limbs to bring the muscles back into action. It was also used in this manner for any malady in which it was desirable to bring the blood to the surface to relieve vital organs.

Nettle greens have been used as food both here and in Europe. In addition the stalks yield a tough fiber as good as hemp. It has been used by the Indians for nets and by the Russians for the manufacture of cloth, paper, nets, and rope.

DUTCHMAN'S PIPE FAMILY, Aristolochiaceae

Wild ginger, *Asarum caudatum* Lindl.

Low herb with a creeping rootstock; leaves heart-shaped, palmately veined, paired at the end of the rootstock; flowers borne close to the ground; sepals 3, deep red to brown, tapering to a long tail, each sepal with 2 round, light areas on the inner surface; petals absent; stamens 12.

Moist shaded woods; Coast Range and east to Idaho. The heart-shaped leaves are common everywhere in the woods but the flowers are rarely seen since they lie close to the ground and are frequently covered by leaves and forest debris. Wild ginger is one of our best native wild plants for garden planting where green foliage is desired.

BUCKWHEAT FAMILY, Polygonaceae

Dock, *Rumex*

Herbs with grooved stems; leaves alternate and basal with paperlike stipules sheathing the stem; flowers green or reddish yellow, in panicles; sepals 6, the outer 3 spreading, the inner 3 erect, often bearing a corky protuberance on the back. As the fruit develops, the 3 inner sepals also enlarge and enclose the fruit. The docks are among our most troublesome garden weeds.

Key to Species

1 Stamens and pistils on separate plants; leaves with earlike lobes
      at the base   Sour dock, *R. acetosella*
1 Stamens and pistils in the same flower; leaves tapered or squared
      at the base
    2 At least some of the inner sepals with corky protuberances
      3 Flowers in distinct whorls forming an interrupted inflorescence; usually all the inner sepals with corky grains
                                    Green dock, *R. conglomeratus*
      3 Flowers in close whorls, not forming an interrupted inflorescence; not all the inner sepals with corky grains
                                        Curly dock, *R. crispus*
    2 None of the inner sepals with corky protuberances
                                    Western dock, *R. occidentalis*

Red sorrel or sour dock, *Rumex acetosella* L.
    Perennial herb with reddish stems; lower leaves oval to lanceolate with two earlike lobes at the base; upper leaves narrower and often with the lobes absent; stipules papery; flowers minute; pistils and stamens on different plants; staminate inflorescence yellowish red; pistillate flowers reddish.
    Widespread weed in this country and in Europe. The leaves contain oxalic acid and are acid to the taste. Many people like to chew the leaves, and they are sometimes used in salads and soups, or as a vegetable.

Besides sour dock, three other species of *Rumex* are sometimes in blossom in early June. These are *R. conglomeratus* Murr, *R. crispus* L., and *R. occidentalis* Wats. All are much larger than sour dock.

PURSLANE FAMILY, Portulacaceae

Fleshy herbs with simple leaves; sepals usually 2; petals generally 5, separate or slightly united at the base, stamens 3 to many, opposite the petals when of the same number; ovary superior; fruit a capsule.

Montia

Key to Species

1 Leaves alternate, all alike, long and narrow
                    Narrow-leaved montia, *M. linearis*
1 Leaves opposite and basal, not all alike
    2 Stem leaves united, forming a rounded circle below the flowers   Miner's lettuce, *M. perfoliata*
    2 Stem leaves not united, broad, sessile
                    Candy flower, *M. sibirica*

Narrow-leaved montia, *Montia linearis* (Dougl.) Greene
    Low plant with alternate, narrow leaves attached directly to the stem; flowers 4 to 9 in a raceme, nearly all turning in the same direction; sepals 2, green with white edges; petals 5, white, longer than the sepals; seeds shiny black, round, flat. As the seeds ripen, the stems and sepals become red and the flowers turn downward.
    Wet open fields; British Columbia to southern California and east to Montana and Nevada.

Miner's lettuce, *Montia perfoliata* (Donn) Howell
    Succulent plant, 4 to 12 inches tall; stems many, arising from the base; basal leaves long and narrow, wider at the tip, tapering to the base; stem leaves 2, united, forming a circle around the stem at the base of the flower cluster; flowers small with 2 sepals and 5 white or pinkish petals.
    Open woods; west coast to Idaho and Arizona.

Candy flower. *Montia sibirica*

Candy flower, *Montia sibirica* (L.) Howell
Whole plant juicy and brittle, 4 to 20 inches high; stems several, arising from the base of the plant; basal leaves with a long leaf stalk; stem leaves 2, attached directly to the stem below the flower cluster; flowers white to pink; sepals 2; petals 5, notched, with dark red stripes.

Moist woods; eastern Siberia to Alaska and from Alaska south to California and east to Montana and Idaho. Although this is one of the earliest blossoming plants in the spring, flowers can still be found as late as August and September.

PINK FAMILY, Caryophyllaceae

Herbs with opposite leaves and stems usually swollen at the joints; sepals and petals generally 5; stamens 5 or 10; ovary superior; fruit a capsule.

Sandwort, *Arenaria macrophylla* Hook.
Slender plant, 2 to 5 inches tall; leaves opposite, long and narrow; flowers white, 1 to 5 at the end of the stem or branch; sepals 5; petals 5, as long as the sepals; stamens 10.

Coniferous woods; west of the Cascades and eastward to the Great Lakes.

Annual mouse-ear chickweed, *Cerastium viscosum* L.
Branching plant, hairy, often sticky; leaves opposite, sessile, oval, rounded at the apex; flowers in dense clusters, the flower stems shorter than the flowers; petals white, about as long as the sepals or longer.

A common introduced garden weed, now widespread across the continent.

Common mouse-ear chickweed, *Cerastium vulgatum* L.
Stems branching, spreading, often forming a wide mat; whole plant hairy; leaves opposite, elongated, narrow; flowers small, white, borne on flower stems longer than the flower; sepals as long as the petals.

Introduced lawn weed, very common from coast to coast. The two mouse-ear chickweeds are distinguished by differences in leaf shape: *C. viscosum* has short oval leaves, and *C. vulgatum* has elongated narrow leaves. There are also differences in length of each individual flower stalk, the stalk in *C. vulgatum* being longer than the flower.

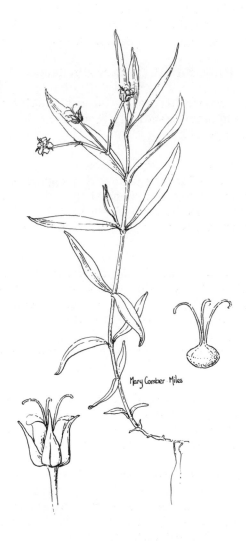

Sandwort. *Arenaria macrophylla*

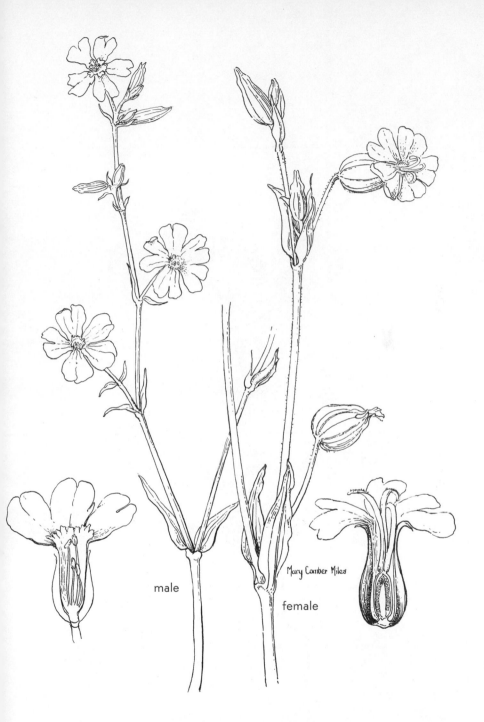

male

female

Mary Comber Miles

White cockle or white campion. *Lychnis alba*

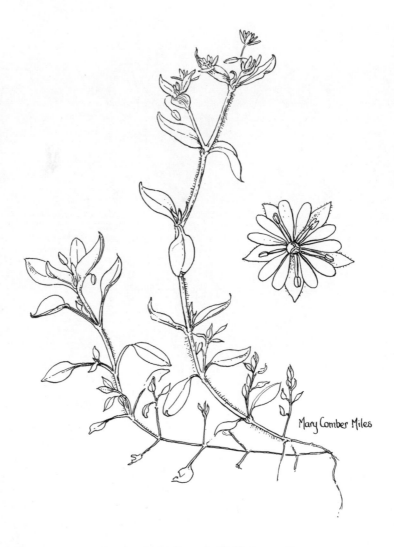

Mary Comber Miles

Common chickweed. *Stellaria media*.

White cockle or white campion, *Lychnis alba* Mill.

Plants branched, 2 feet or more in height; leaves opposite, oval to lance-shaped, hairy; sepals 5, hairy, united at the base, bearing 10 distinct veins; petals white, deeply 2-cleft, spreading at right angles above the calyx, each with a small projection at the bending point; stamens and pistils on separate plants; stamens 10 of variable lengths; pistil with 5 styles. As the ovary enlarges in fruit, the calyx becomes inflated and the petals wither.

Introduced from Europe, this plant has spread through California and is becoming common around Portland.

Corn spurry, *Spergula arvensis* L.

Plant branching at the base into several erect stems; leaves very narrow, appearing whorled; flowers on wide-spreading stems, turning downward in fruit; sepals 5; petals 5, white, about as long as the sepals; seeds round, dull black with a narrow, light-colored margin.

Corn spurry is a weed of corn fields all over Europe and temperate Asia, and it is widespread in the Pacific Northwest. It occurs in grain fields, orchards, and gardens.

Pink sand spurry, *Spergularia rubra* (L.) J. and C. Presl

Small herb branching from the base, forming a dense mat 6 to 20 inches across; leaves linear, about 1/2 inch long, minutely spine-tipped; stipules papery; flowers pink; sepals 5, soft-hairy, with papery margins; petals 5, about as long as the sepals; stamens 6 to 10.

On dry ground; introduced from Europe and common from Puget Sound to southern California and in the eastern states.

Common chickweed, *Stellaria media* (L.) Cyrill.

Weak, much-branched plant, rooting at the lower nodes, smooth except for a line of hairs along one side of the stem; leaves opposite, ovate, upper leaves sessile; lower leaves with petioles; flowers white, on stalks at first very short but becoming long and slender; sepals 5; petals 5, deeply notched, shorter than the sepals.

This chickweed is introduced from Europe, and it is now a common weed throughout North America. It grows best in moist shady places where it may cover wide areas. The blossoms appear in April and can still be found in August and September.

Mary Comber Miles

Baneberry. *Actaea arguta*

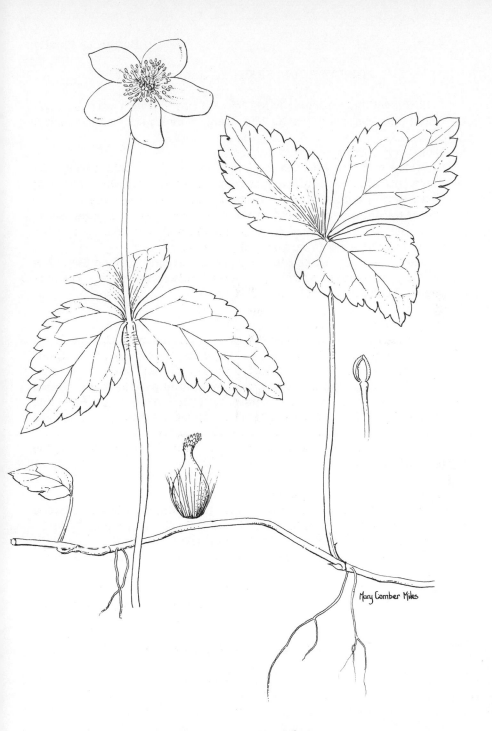

Windflower. *Anemone deltoidea*

BUTTERCUP FAMILY, Ranunculaceae

Herbs with alternate or basal leaves; flowers with parts all separate; stamens many; pistils 1 to many, simple; fruit dry or fleshy.

Baneberry, *Actaea arguta* Nutt.
Herb 1 to 3 feet tall; leaves 1 to 3 on the stem, 3 to 4 times divided into threes; leaflets sharp-pointed and coarsely toothed; flowers in a dense raceme at the end of the stem, one or more flowers sometimes present in the upper leaf axils; sepals white, petal-like, 3 to 5, falling early; petals often absent; stamens many; pistil 1; fruit a large red or white berry.
Shaded woods; Alaska to California and east to Montana. The bright red berries, which are ripe in July and August, are poisonous but animals seldom eat them.

Windflower, *Anemone deltoidea* Hook.
Plants 5 to 11 inches high; stems single from a slender rootstock; stem leaves 3 in a whorl below the flower, ovate, toothed above the middle; flower 1 inch or more across, on a long stalk; sepals 5, white; petals absent; stamens and pistils many. Basal leaves also arise from the rootstock. These are long-petioled and divided into 3 toothed leaflets. These leaves are few in number and often are not seen when the flower is in blossom.
Moist coniferous woods; west of the Cascades from Washington to California.

Columbine, *Aquilegia formosa* Fisch.
Erect, 1 to 3 feet tall, branching; leaves mostly basal, divided into 3 parts, these again divided into 3 leaflets; leaflets 2- or 3-cleft with narrow lobes; flowers solitary in leaf axils; sepals 5, red; petals 5, spurred, the spur red and the blade yellow; stamens many; pistils 5.
Open woods; Alaska to California and east to Montana and Utah. This graceful plant is one of our most attractive native wild flowers.

Larkspur, *Delphinium*

Key to species

1 Flowers white   White larkspur, *D. leucophaeum*
1 Flowers blue

Columbine. *Aquilegia formosa*

Mary Comber Miles

Wood larkspur. *Delphinium trolliifolium*

2 Plants less than 2 feet tall; spur straight
                            Field larkspur, *D. menziesii*
2 Plants 2 to 5 feet tall; spur curved
                            Wood larkspur, *D. trolliifolium*

White larkspur, *Delphinium leucophaeum* Greene
   Erect perennial herb, 10 to 30 inches tall, usually hairy; leaves
long-stalked, with 3 to 5 divisions, these again divided 3 or more
times; racemes 6- to 12-flowered; sepals creamy white, the upper one with a straight or upcurved spur; lower petals white, the
upper petals generally a bright blue.
   Fields; Willamette Valley. The white larkspur is generally found
growing in the same vicinity as *Delphinium menziesii* and for this
reason has been named *D. menziesii* var. *ochroleucum*.

Field larkspur, *Delphinium menziesii* DC.
   Plants 8 to 24 inches tall, branching; leaves palmately cut almost to the petiole, the divisions further cut into narrow segments;
flowers in a raceme, dark blue; sepals 5, the upper one with a long
straight spur; petals 4, in 2 pairs, the upper pair extending backward into the calyx; stamens many; pistils 3.
   Open fields; west of the Cascades from British Columbia to California.

Wood larkspur, *Delphinium trolliifolium* Gray
   Large branching plant, 2 to 5 feet tall; stems hollow; leaves palmately cut into segments, these with coarse teeth; flowers blue;
spur of the upper sepal generally curved.
   Moist places, usually in the shade of trees; from the Willamette
Valley to California. The two blue species of larkspur can be distinguished by their habitat, size, and nature of the root system.
Field larkspur has a cluster of fleshy roots, whereas wood larkspur has hard, woody, slender roots. There is usually a difference
in the spur of the calyx also, field larkspur having a straight spur
and wood larkspur a curved spur.
   All the species of *Delphinium* are poisonous to cattle. Sheep can
graze these plants without serious harm, but cattle develop stag-
gers, an abnormal thirst, and retarded heart action.

Woods buttercup. *Ranunculus bongardii*

Field buttercup. *Ranunculus occidentalis*

Buttercup, *Ranunculus*

Key to Species

1 Flowers small, pale yellow, usually with only 2 or 3 petals
                          Woods buttercup, *R. bongardii*
1 Flowers 1/2 inch across, bright yellow, usually with 5 petals
    2 Lower leaves divided into 3 leaflets; petals broad
                          Creeping buttercup, *R. repens*
    2 Lower leaves deeply cut but not compound; petals oblong
                          Field buttercup, *R. occidentalis*

Woods buttercup, *Ranunculus bongardii* Greene
    Stems reaching 2 feet in height, hairy; lower leaves deeply cut
into 3 parts, these lobed and coarsely toothed, hairy; upper leaves
often narrow without teeth; flowers small, pale yellow with 2 to
5 petals.
    Moist woods; Alaska, northern Rockies, and California. The
plant is often large and husky but the flowers are pale, small and
inconspicuous. It is common throughout the woods of our area.

Field buttercup, *Ranunculus occidentalis* Nutt.
    Stems several from the base, usually hairy; basal leaves deep-
ly cut into 3 to 5 parts, these further lobed and toothed, hairy;
upper leaves cut into several narrow divisions; flowers bright
yellow with 5 oblong petals.
    Moist fields; west of the Cascades. The field buttercup is not
common in the immediate vicinity of Portland, but farther south
the fields of the Willamette Valley are golden with this flower in
the spring.

Creeping buttercup, *Ranunculus repens* L.
    Stems creeping, rooting at the nodes and sending up upright
branches, hairy; lower leaves with 3 leaflets, each leaflet 3-lobed
and deeply toothed; upper leaves smaller, deeply cut but not compound; flowers yellow; petals broad.
    Naturalized from Europe in western Oregon. This is the most
common buttercup in our area. It is large and rank along streams
and wet shady places, smaller in the open, along roadsides. It is
a persistent lawn weed in some areas. The creeping habit is often not easily seen, but it becomes apparent if the plant is dug up
or examined closely.

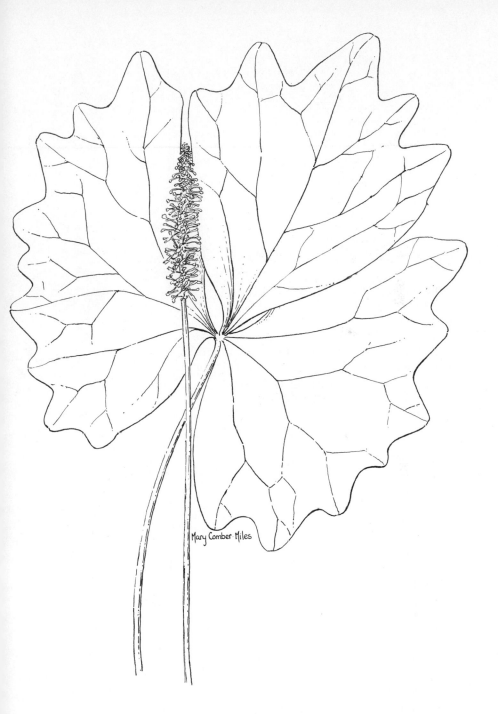

Vanilla leaf. *Achlys triphylla*

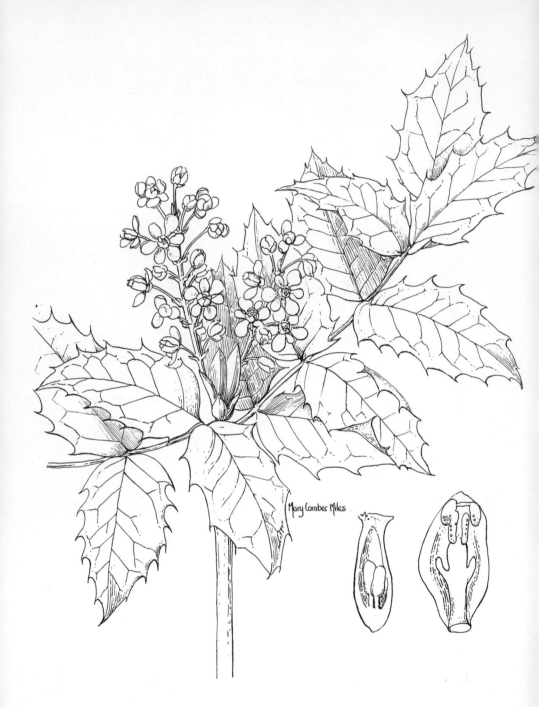

Oregon grape. *Berberis aquifolium*

Western meadow rue, *Thalictrum occidentale* Gray
Perennial herb, 15 to 36 inches tall; leaves divided several times
in threes; leaflets thin, round or oblong, 3-lobed at the apex; pistils and stamens on separate plants; staminate flowers greenish,
the stamens hanging tassel-like beyond the sepals; pistils 5 or 6,
with purple styles; petals absent.
Moist shaded woods; British Columbia to northern California
and east to Alberta, Montana, and Utah. Although the flowers are
small and inconspicuous the delicate fernlike foliage makes this
a very attractive plant.

BARBERRY FAMILY, Berberidaceae

Herbs or shrubs with alternate or basal compound leaves; sepals
6 or absent; petals 6 or absent; stamens 6, opposite the petals,
or many; pistil 1, simple, superior; fruit dry or fleshy.

Vanilla leaf, *Achlys triphylla* (Sm.) DC.
Leaves and flower stalks separately arising from an underground
rootstock; leaves 10 to 18 inches high, often 10 to 12 inches across,
divided into 3 leaflets; leaflets broad and scalloped at the top, tapering to a point at the base; flowers in a dense spike, rising above
the leaves; sepals and petals absent; stamens many, white.
Common in fir woods; west of the Cascades from British Columbia to California. A sweet, vanillalike fragrance is given off as the
foliage withers, and a vanilla substitute has been extracted from
the leaves.

Oregon grape, *Berberis aquifolium* Pursh
Evergreen shrub, 2 to 8 feet in height; leaves pinnately compound with 5 to 9 leaflets; leaflets leathery, stiff, with stout spines
on the margins; flowers yellow, in racemes at the end of the stem
and in the upper leaf axils; flowers with 3 yellow bracts at the
base; flower parts all opposite and yellow; sepals 6; petals 6;
stamens 6.
Woods and open areas; mostly west of the Cascades from British Columbia to California. This species was designated the state
flower of Oregon by the legislature in 1899. The blue berries are
used by some housewives to make jelly, which is said to have a
delicious wild-grape flavor. The Indians used the fruit and also
the bark, from which they extracted a yellow dye. The bark of the
root is of medicinal value.

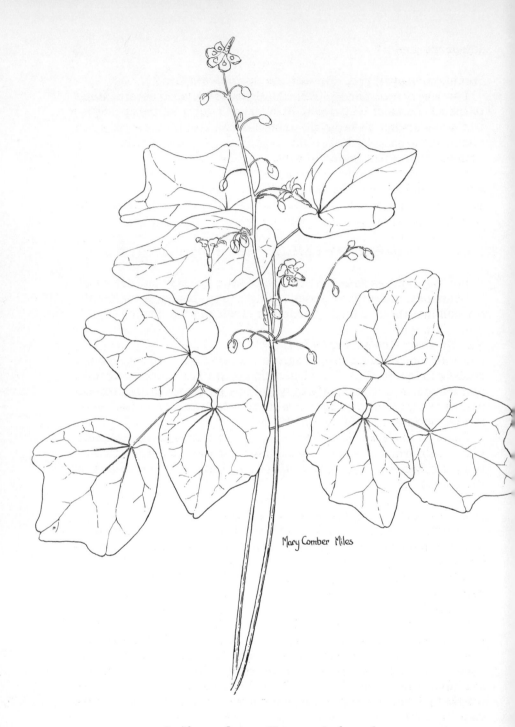

Inside-out flower. *Vancouveria hexandra*

Mountain Oregon grape, *Berberis nervosa* Pursh

Low evergreen shrub, under 2 feet tall; leaves pinnately compound with 9 to 21 leaflets; leaflets thick, leathery, spiny, with 3 to 5 veins arising from the base; flowers yellow, in racemes at the end of the stems.

Coniferous woods; west of the Cascades from British Columbia to California. Another name for this species is long-leaved Oregon grape. In addition to the differences in plant size, the two species of Oregon grape can be distinguished on the basis of the leaf characters. *B. aquifolium* has fewer leaflets, and each is pinnately veined. The leaflets of *B. nervosa* have 3 to 5 veins arising from the base.

Inside-out flower, *Vancouveria hexandra* (Hook.) Morr. and Dcne.

Leaves and flower stems 8 to 24 inches high; leaves 2 or 3 times divided into threes; leaflets heart-shaped at the base, 1- to 3-angled; flowers white, drooping, in a wide-spreading panicle; sepals 6, sharply turned backward, conspicuous; petals 6, smaller, opposite the sepals and lying close against them; stamens 6, protruding forward and surrounding the pistil. In bud it can be seen that there are 6 to 9 small bracts at the base of the sepals. These disappear when the flower opens. Minute glands dot the stamen filaments and the ovary.

Common in shady, moist woods; west of the Cascades, Washington to California. The genus is named for Captain George Vancouver, who explored Puget Sound and the lower Columbia between 1790 and 1795.

POPPY FAMILY, Papaveraceae

California poppy, *Eschscholtzia californica* Cham.

Plants 6 to 18 inches high; basal leaves long-stalked, grayish green, divided into long, narrow segments; stem leaves smaller with short petioles; flowers single at the end of the stem, yellow or orange; sepals 2, large, falling off as the flower opens; petals 4, rounded; stamens many; pistil 1.

Fields and roadsides; Willamette Valley to California. This is the state flower of California and it is widespread throughout that state. It is quite common around Portland, growing in open fields and along roadsides.

In 1817 a Russian expedition cast anchor off San Francisco. With the expedition were two naturalists, Adelbert von Chamisso, a botanist, and Johann Eschscholtz, a surgeon-zoologist. The poppy

California poppy. *Eschscholtzia californica*

Western corydalis. *Corydalis scouleri*

Bleeding heart. *Dicentra formosa*

was named by Chamisso for his friend. Like other members of
the poppy family the juice of the plant contains a narcotic principle.
The Indians are said to have made use of this fact, and as a rem-
edy for toothache they placed a portion of poppy root on the sore
tooth. The plant is an important source of golden pollen for bees.

BLEEDING HEART FAMILY, Fumariaceae

Perennial herbs with much-divided, compound leaves; flowers
irregular; sepals 2, small; petals 4 in 2 pairs; stamens in 2 sets
of 3, united by the filaments; fruit a capsule.

Western corydalis, *Corydalis scouleri* Hook.
Plants reaching 3 to 4 feet in height; leaves 2 or 3 times pinnately compound, the leaflets oblong, entire or deeply lobed; flowers
pink, in a long raceme; corolla with a single long spur.
Not common; moist woods and along streams; northern Cascades
and Coast Ranges from the Olympic Penninsula to Tillamook, Oregon. Look for this plant along creeks in fir woods associated with
bleeding heart. The specific name honors Dr. John Scouler, who
came to the mouth of the Columbia in 1825 with David Douglas and
collected along the Pacific Coast as far north as Nootka on Vancouver Island.

Bleeding heart, *Dicentra formosa* (Andr.) DC.
Leaves and flower stalks arising separately from an underground
stem; leaves divided twice into threes, the leaflets pinnately cut
and lobed; flowers purplish pink, drooping, on stalks taller than
the leaves; sepals 2; petals 4, in 2 pairs; stamens 6, in 2 sets of 3.
Moist woods; Cascades and Coast Ranges from British Columbia
to California. Except for its smaller size and paler colors, the
wild bleeding heart quite closely resembles the cultivated form,
Dicentra spectabilis. It is an attractive addition to the shady flower bed.

MUSTARD FAMILY, Cruciferae

Herbs with alternate leaves; flowers having 4 sepals and 4 petals; stamens generally 6, 4 long and 2 short; fruit dry, usually
splitting to expose a central partition with seeds attached on each
side.
The numbers of sepals, petals, and stamens make the mustard
family easily recognizable, but the determination of the genera and

species is a difficult task. The distinguishing characters are based on the seed pod, and it is therefore necessary to have the fruit in order to make a positive identification. Fortunately, the fruit is often present with flowers on the same plant.

Rock Cress, *Arabis*

Key to Species

1 Flowers showy, 1/2 to 3/4 inch across
                            Rock cress, *A. albida*
1 Flowers not showy, very small
  2 Plants 2 to 4 feet tall, not hairy
                            Tower mustard, *A. glabra*
  2 Plants less than 2 feet tall; hairy throughout
                            Hairy rock cress, *A. hirsuta*

Rock cress, *Arabis albida* Stev.
    Plants 3 to 10 inches tall, branching, grayish green, sparingly to woolly-hairy, the hairs star-shaped; lower leaves petioled, widest above the middle, tapering to the base, coarsely toothed; stem leaves pointed at the tip, clasping the stem and eared at the base; flowers white, showy, 1/2 to 3/4 inch across, in racemes flat at the top; calyx light green, turning yellow with age; seed pod slightly flattened, long, linear.
    This cultivated rock plant has occasionally escaped and become established locally.

Tower mustard, *Arabis glabra* (L.) Bernh.
    Biennial, 2 to 4 feet tall, usually unbranched; lower leaves widest above the middle, tapering toward the base, toothed to lobed on the margins; stem leaves narrow, clasping the stem and eared at the base; flowers greenish white to yellowish, very small; pods narrow, erect.
    Fields and open woods; widely distributed in the United States.

Hairy rock cress, *Arabis hirsuta* (L.) Scop.
    Erect herb, 8 to 20 inches tall, unbranched, hairy; basal leaves spatula-shaped, tapering at the base into the petiole, entire or slightly toothed on the margin; stem leaves sessile, narrower, obtuse or acute at the apex, often with earlike projections at the base; flowers small, white; seed pods up to 2 1/2 inches long.

In rocky places or in woods; Alaska to New Brunswick, south to California and east to Georgia; also in Europe and Asia.

Winter cress, *Barbarea orthoceras* Ledeb.

Plants erect, 1 to 2 feet tall; leaves pinnately divided into 5 to 7 lobes, the terminal segment much longer and rounded on the basal leaves, narrower and pointed on the upper leaves; stem leaves clasping at the base; flowers yellow, in a raceme at the end of the stem; seed pods linear, slightly spreading from the stem.

Moist places; British Columbia to Montana and south to Lower California; native to North America. This plant resembles common yellow mustard. However, on examination of the leaves, it will be seen that all the leaves of winter cress are pinnately divided while the stem leaves of mustard are simple.

The Latin name *Barbarea* is derived from the belief that the young leaves are green and edible on St. Barbara's Day. The young stems and leaves are said to taste much like dandelions.

Yellow mustard, *Brassica campestris* L.

Erect plant 1 to 3 feet tall, branching; lower leaves with leaf-stalks pinnately cut into irregular lobes, the terminal lobe large and irregularly toothed; stem simple, not toothed, clasping the stem; flowers in a raceme which elongates as the flowers open; petals 4, yellow; stamens 6, 4 long and 2 short; seed pod spreading from the stem, 1 to 2 1/2 inches long, cylindrical.

Common along roadsides and in fields; introduced from Europe. During a mild winter one often sees yellow mustard in blossom in January. In the Willamette Valley yellow mustard is a producer of considerable nectar, and is very attractive to bees.

Shepherd's purse, *Capsella bursa-pastoris* (L.) Medic.

Stem erect, branching, arising from a rosette of leaves; basal leaves elongated, wider above the middle, entire or slightly dentate to deeply cut, petioled; stem leaves narrow, clasping the stem; leaves and stem with star-shaped hairs; flowers white, very small, borne on a flower stem which elongates as the fruit matures; seed pod triangular, notched at the top.

This is a garden weed of almost world-wide distribution. There is great variation in the size and shape of the lower leaves. In the early 1800's the plant was cultivated in Philadelphia for use as a pot herb.

Yellow mustard. *Brassica campestris*

Bitter cress. *Cardamine oligosperma*

Wood bitter cress, *Cardamine angulata* Hook.

Upright herb, 1 to 2 feet tall, not branched; leaves divided into 3 to 5 leaflets; leaflets 2- to 5-angled; upper leaves with a larger terminal leaflet or sometimes simple, entire or toothed on the margin; all leaves petioled; flowers about 1/2 inch across, in a raceme at first compact, later elongating as the lower flowers wither; petals 4, white.

Shady moist places, generally along streams; northern Oregon and Washington. The flowers are much more showy than any of the other species of *Cardamine*.

Bitter cress, *Cardamine oligosperma* Nutt.

Stems usually branching from a basal rosette of leaves; leaves pinnately compound with 5 to 10 leaflets; leaflets of the lower leaves roundish, toothed or entire, distinctly stalked, upper leaflets becoming more elongated and less distinctly stalked; flowers minute, white; seed pod slender, about 1 inch long at maturity.

Moist ground; west of the Cascades from British Columbia and Idaho to southern California. In many areas of Portland this is a common garden and field weed. It can also be seen in shady woods, where it may reach 12 to 15 inches in height. Blossoms may be found in February and all through the spring and summer.

Spring beauty, *Dentaria tenella* Pursh

Stem erect, 4 to 10 inches tall, from a tuberous rootstock; basal leaves rounded, long-petioled, the margins wavy; stem leaves usually one or two, divided into 3 to 5 narrow segments with smooth edges; flowers pinkish lavender; stamens 6, seed pods long, cylindrical. The basal leaves are often at a distance from the flowering stem, and one frequently sees a group of basal leaves but no flowers. There is considerable variation in this species. Sometimes the basal leaf is deeply lobed or even compound, and the stem leaves vary from 1 to 3 with 3 to 5 divisions present.

Moist open woods; west of the Cascades from British Columbia to Josephine County, Oregon.

Whitlow grass, *Draba verna* L.

Annual herb, 1 1/2 to 6 inches tall; leaves basal, oval to oblong, with a few marginal teeth; petals white, notched to the middle, about twice as long as the sepals; pod oblong-elliptic, less than 3 times as long as wide.

Introduced from Europe and now abundant on the Pacific Coast from British Columbia to northern California.

Mary Comber Miles.

Spring beauty. *Dentaria tenella*

Wallflower, *Erysimum arkansanum* Nutt.

Stem erect, simple or branched, generally 8 to 24 inches tall, whole plant hairy; leaves long and narrow, somewhat toothed, with a petiole at the base of the plant, sessile above; flowers orange, 1/2 to 1 inch long, in racemes; pod 4-sided, covered with hairs.

Wooded slopes; from Washington to California and east to the Mississippi Valley.

Rocket or dame's violet, *Hesperis matronalis* L.

Erect, branching herb, 1 to 3 feet high; leaves elongated, tapering to a point at the tip and at the base, short-petioled or the upper leaves sessile, toothed on the margins; flowers showy, 1/2 to 1 1/4 inches across, lavender, or nearly white, fragrant, especially at night; seed pods spreading, 2 to 4 inches long, narrow, cylindrical, constricted between the seeds.

This is a common old-fashioned garden plant which has escaped and can be found along the roadsides in many places around Portland. The name, *Hesperis,* is from the Greek *hesperos,* evening, and refers to the evening fragrance of the flower.

Honesty, *Lunaria annua* L.

Large plant 2 to 4 feet tall, branched; leaves alternate, heart-shaped or triangular, hairy, with jagged margins; petioles present; flowers purple or sometimes white, 1/2 to 1 inch across, showy; mature seed pods oval, very thin, becoming silvery white.

Honesty has become well established around Portland as an escaped garden plant. It has long been a favorite in cultivation for its colorful flowers and large, silvery fruits which are used in dry bouquets. The name comes from the fact that the seeds can be seen through the pod. Other common names are: money plant, silver dollar plant, and moonwort because of the resemblance to money and to the full moon.

Jointed charlock, *Raphanus raphanistrum* L.

Plants similar in appearance to wild radish except flowers yellow to white, veined with black; fruit long and narrow, constricted between the 4 to 7 seeds like a chain of beads.

Fields and roadsides; naturalized from Europe.

Wild radish, *Raphanus sativus* L.

Plants 1 1/2 to 3 feet tall, branching; lower leaves pinnately divided with a large terminal segment and numerous lateral segments of many sizes, upper leaves with fewer segments or undivided, all leaves toothed and hairy; flowers in racemes; petals about 3/4 inch long, white to lavender or pink, with distinct veins of deep purple; seed pod 1 to 3 inches long, pithy, wide at the base, constricted between the 2 or 3 seeds, tapered to a sharp, long point at the apex, not splitting to discharge the seeds.

Common weed of fields and roadsides; naturalized from Europe.

Hedge mustard, *Sisymbrium officinale* (L.) Scop.

Herb, 1 to 4 feet high, usually with wide-spreading branches, more or less hairy; leaves pinnately cut, the upper segment larger, lower segments pointing downward, all segments somewhat toothed; leaves with leafstalks; flowers pale yellow, very small; seed pods narrow, about 1/2 inch long, closely pressed against the stem.

Roadsides; introduced from Europe and spread throughout North America. Its close, appressed seed pods and petioled leaves readily distinguish it from the other mustardlike flowers of this area.

STONECROP FAMILY, Crassulaceae

Douglas' stonecrop, *Sedum douglasii* Hook.

Flowering stems erect, spreading, 4 to 8 or 9 inches tall, leafy; leaves narrow, flattened, acute at the apex, broad at the base, at first fleshy, then becoming dry and papery; flowers yellow; petals narrow, longer than the stamens; pistils 5, widely spreading.

On rocky banks, not common in western Oregon and Washington; from British Columbia to California.

Broad-leaved stonecrop, *Sedum spathulifolium* Hook.

Leaves in rosettes at the ends of stolons that branch from the main stem, thick, fleshy, broadly spoon-shaped, covered with a whitish bloom; flower-bearing stem erect or reclining, 4 to 8 inches long, leafy; flowers yellow, in a cyme bearing fleshy bracts; petals 5, twice as long as the sepals; stamens 10; pistils 5, not spreading.

Wet rocky banks; west of the Cascades from British Columbia to California. The stonecrops are propagated vegetatively by means of the stolons which develop rosettes of fleshy leaves.

SAXIFRAGE FAMILY, Saxifragaceae

Perennial herbs and shrubs; sepals 5, partly united; petals 5, attached to the tube of the united sepals; stamens 5 or 10; ovary superior or inferior; fruit dry or fleshy.

Small-flowered alumroot, *Heuchera micrantha* Dougl.

Flower stem 1 to 3 feet tall, arising from a cluster of long-petioled basal leaves; leaves shiny, roundish to oblong, heart-shaped at the base, palmately veined, toothed and shallowly lobed on the margins; petioles hairy, reddish; stem leaves few, with shorter petioles; flowers in a wide-spreading panicle, small; calyx 5-lobed, white; petals smaller, white; stamens 5 with orange anthers.

Moist places, especially on wet rocky cliffs; west of the Cascades from southern British Columbia to California. A beautiful display of this plant can be seen on the rocky banks bordering Germantown Road in northwest Portland. The root is said to have astringent properties; hence the common name.

Ragged starflower, *Lithophragma parviflora* (Hook.) Nutt.

Stem slender, erect, 6 to 18 inches tall; basal leaves round in outline, 3- to 5-lobed, the lobes cut and toothed; stem leaves 1 to 3, small, 3-parted, the divisions further lobed; flowers pink to white, in a raceme; petals deeply 3-cleft; stamens 10; pistil with 3 styles.

Open ground; British Columbia to California, east to Colorado.

Leafy-stemmed bishop's-cap, *Mitella caulescens* Nutt.

Stem 6 to 15 inches high, bearing 1 to 3 leaves; basal leaves long-petioled, 3-lobed, hairy, cordate at the base, round-toothed on the margins; flowers in an elongated inflorescence, blossoming from the top down; calyx lobes green; petals green, deep purple at the base, pinnately divided into fine segments; stamens 5, with purple filaments.

Wet places; west of the Cascades from northern Oregon to British Columbia. A distinctive characteristic of this genus is the fact that the inflorescence blossoms from the top to the bottom.

Mock orange, *Philadelphus gordonianus* Lindl.

Shrub 5 to 12 feet tall; leaves opposite, ovate, entire or slightly toothed on the margins, 3- to 5-veined from the base or near the base; flowers white, fragrant, 3/4 to 1 inch across; petals and sepals 4; stamens many; ovary inferior.

Open woods west of the Cascades from British Columbia to northern California. The large, white, fragrant blossoms make this shrub popular as an ornamental. A closely related species of *Philadelphus* is the state flower of Idaho. Usually mock orange does not blossom until late June or July, but in an occasional early year the blossoms are out by the middle of June.

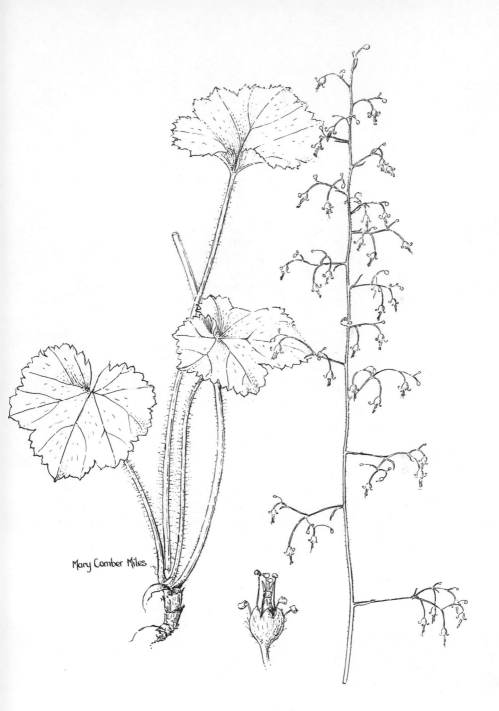

Mary Comber Miles

Small-flowered alumroot. *Heuchera micrantha*

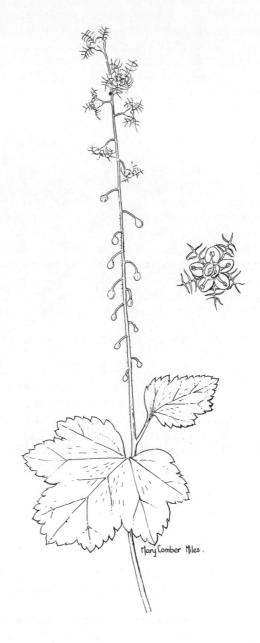

Leafy-stemmed bishop's-cap. *Mitella caulescens*

Stinking currant, *Ribes bracteosum* Dougl.

Shrub reaching 15 feet in shady locations; stems tannish, without prickles; leaves large, 5 to 9 inches wide, 3- to 5-lobed, the lobes sharp at the apex and doubly serrate, palmately veined; leaves, petioles, and calyx with glandular hairs; flowers in long racemes; calyx green, the lobes turned backward; petals greenish, much smaller than the sepals.

Along streams in shady places; west of the Cascades from British Columbia to California. Smell the broken stems and leaves of this plant and you will agree that the common name is well-chosen!

Red-flowering currant, *Ribes sanguineum* Pursh

Shrub, 4 to 8 feet tall; stems brown; leaves roundish in outline, 3- to 5-lobed, palmately veined, minutely toothed; flowers showy, red to pink, in drooping racemes; sepals red, larger than the petals; petals pale pink to white.

Open woods and roadsides; west of the Cascades from British Columbia to northern California. This is an early blooming, beautiful native shrub. Here we can enjoy this colorful shrub and know that it does no damage. In white pine country, however, all currant and gooseberry bushes must be pulled up within a distance of 900 feet of the pines, since these plants serve as the alternate host for the white pine blister rust which has done considerable damage in the Northwest.

Broad-leaved saxifrage, *Saxifraga integrifolia* Hook.

Leaves all basal, 2 to 3 inches long, broadly ovate or oblong, rounded at the apex and tapering at the base to the petiole, somewhat toothed on the margin; flower stalks 1/2 to 1 foot or more tall, covered with reddish, glandular hairs; flowers in tight clusters, white.

Moist banks and fields; west of the Cascades from Washington to Oregon and east along the Columbia River to eastern Washington and Oregon.

Oregon saxifrage, *Saxifraga oregana* Howell

Leaves basal, spreading, 2 to 6 inches or more in length, ovate or widest above the middle, tapering to the base without a definite petiole; flower stalk 12 to 40 inches tall, hollow, glandular; flowers in close clusters, white.

Very wet places; northwestern Oregon to Washington and east to Idaho, central Oregon and western Nevada. This species can be

Red-flowering currant. *Ribes sanguineum*

distinguished from broad-leaved saxifrage by its large size, by
the absence of a distinct petiole, and by the hollow flower stalk.

Fringe cup, *Tellima grandiflora* (Pursh) Dougl.
Flower stems 1 to 2 feet tall, from a cluster of long-petioled
basal leaves; leaves roundish in outline, heart-shaped at the base,
lobed and sharply toothed, long-hairy on the petioles; stem leaves
sessile or nearly so; flowers in a long raceme, all or nearly all
facing the same direction; sepals 5, united into a cup; petals 5,
greenish white to pink or red, much fringed, small, alternating
with the points of the sepals; stamens 10.
Woods; common; Alaska to California, west of the Cascades.

Three-leaved coolwort or laceflower, *Tiarella trifoliata* L.
Plants 10 to 20 inches high, both basal and stem leaves present;
leaves divided into 3 leaflets; leaflets lobed and toothed; flowers
in a long panicle, white; calyx 5-parted, white, glandular; petals
linear, minute; stamens 10, of varying lengths, extending beyond
the sepals and petals; pistil with 2 slender styles, purple-tipped.
Shady, moist woods; in the Cascades and westward from Oregon
to Alaska, and in Asia.

Youth-on-age, *Tolmiea menziesii* (Pursh) T. and G.
Flower stem 10 to 30 inches tall; basal leaves on long petioles;
stem leaves short-petioled, alternate; all leaves heart-shaped,
palmately veined, lobed, hairy, toothed on the margins, having at
the junction of leaf blade and petiole a bud which gives rise to new
growth; flowers in a long raceme; sepals 5, greenish brown, united, the 3 on top of the flower large, 2 on the bottom small with
a deep cleft between them; petals 4, long and hairlike, brownish;
stamens 3, 2 long and 1 short; pistil 1, with 2 stigmas and styles.
Common in moist woods; west of the Cascades from Alaska to
California. The presence of the new growth on the old accounts
for the common name. One can often see this plant for sale in the
garden section of our big super markets under the name of "piggy-
back plant."

ROSE FAMILY, Rosaceae

Trees, shrubs, and herbs with alternate leaves; stipules usually present; sepals generally 5, partly united, often with alternating bractlets; petals 5; stamens commonly 10 or more, attached
with the petals to the cup formed by the united sepals; pistils 1

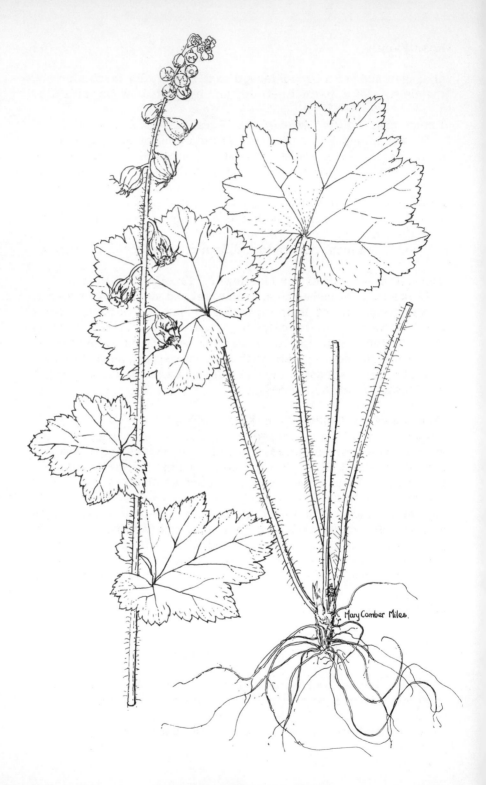

Fringe cup. *Tellima grandiflora*

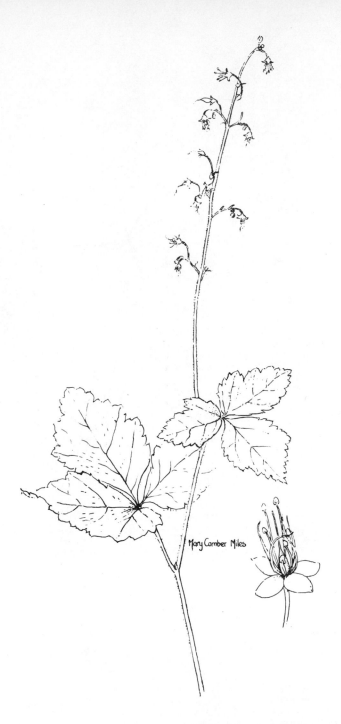

Three-leaved coolwort or laceflower. *Tiarella trifoliata*

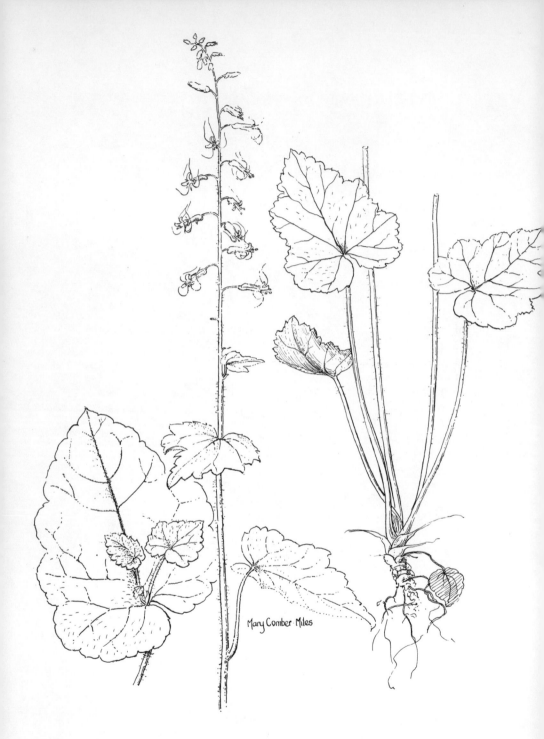

Youth-on-age. *Tolmiea menziesii*

to many, simple or compound and united with the calyx; fruit dry or fleshy.

Serviceberry, *Amelanchier florida* Lindl.

Large shrub, 4 to 15 feet tall; leaves oval, toothed above the middle, pinnately veined; flowers white, in erect dense racemes; calyx 5-parted, united with the ovary; petals 5, long and narrow; stamens many.

Open areas; southern Alaska to California and east to Idaho. According to Haskin in *Wild Flowers of the Pacific Coast,* the Indians valued the straight young shoots of this plant for arrow shafts, and the fruit constituted a staple article of their food when mixed with pounded meat as pemmican.

Goatsbeard, *Aruncus sylvester* Kostel.

Perennial herb 3 to 8 feet tall; leaves pinnately compound, with leaflets 1 1/2 to 4 inches long; leaflets ovate, obtuse at the base, pointed at the apex, toothed; flowers small, creamy white, in terminal panicles; stamens and pistils on different plants.

Moist wooded areas; Alaska to California. Found also from New York to Georgia, and in Europe and Asia. The name *Aruncus* means the beard of a goat, which refers to the long spikes of creamy white flowers. As a cultivated plant it can be very effective, used where one might plant *Spiraea.*

Western hawthorn, *Crataegus douglasii* Lindl.

Shrub or small tree; stems with stout thorns and rough bark; leaves alternate, oval, fan-shaped, toothed, or toothed and lobed above the middle, tapering sharply to the petiole; flowers white, 1/2 inch across, in showy clusters on short leafy shoots; petals rounded; stamens about 20.

Woods and in the open along streams, often forming dense thickets; west of the Cascades from British Columbia to California. The thorns generally keep away livestock, but the young shoots are often eaten by cattle and sheep.

Wood strawberry, *Fragaria bracteata* Heller

Plants with runners, reaching 13 inches or more in height; leaves with 3 leaflets, hairy; margins of leaflets with deep-cut teeth; flower stem usually longer than the leaves, with a single bract resembling a leaflet at the base of the inflorescence.

Open woods; British Columbia to New Mexico. This is our most common strawberry.

Mary Comber Miles

Serviceberry. *Amelanchier florida*

Mary Comber Miles

Wood strawberry. *Fragaria bracteata*

Wild field strawberry, *Fragaria cuneifolia* Nutt.

Low plants with runners; leaves with 3 leaflets, dark green above, lighter and silky-hairy beneath; center leaflet with coarse teeth at the apex; lateral leaflets coarsely toothed at the apex and along the lower margin; petioles hairy; flowers 1 to 6, generally on stems shorter than the leaves, white; flower stem and calyx hairy.

Open hillsides and fields; western Oregon to British Columbia and Idaho.

Large-leaved avens, *Geum macrophyllum* Willd.

Herb 1 to 2 feet tall, hairy; basal leaves long-petioled, pinnately compound with a large, rounded, lobed and toothed leaflet at the top and 3 to 6 pairs of smaller leaflets below; stem leaves with fewer lateral segments and large stipules; flowers yellow; sepals 5, united below into a cup; petals 5 or 6; stamens and pistils many. Mature flowers with petals gone look like spiny balls.

Moist open places or in woods; widely distributed from California to Alaska, Siberia, and Asia. At first glance this flower resembles a buttercup, but a closer look at the flower will reveal the differences. The sepals of the large-leaved avens are united at the base, and 5 bractlets alternate with the 5 calyx lobes. Sepals of buttercups are free from each other, and bracts are absent.

Ocean spray, *Holodiscus discolor* (Pursh) Maxim.

Erect, branched shrub up to 15 or 20 feet tall; leaves ovate, green above, paler and hairy beneath, coarsely toothed or shallowly lobed above the base, rounded at the apex; pinnate venation prominent; flowers very small, creamy white, in large panicles.

Common in thickets; from central California to British Columbia and east to Idaho. Usually ocean spray is not in blossom until late June or July, but occasionally the blossoms will appear by the middle of June. This is one of the woods used by the Indians for arrow shafts. Another common name for the shrub is arrowwood.

Indian peach, *Osmaronia cerasiformis* (T. and G.) Greene

Woody shrub 4 to 12 feet tall; leaves oblong, acute at the apex and tapering at the base, smooth on the margins; flowers in drooping racemes, white or greenish white; stamens and pistils on separate shrubs; pistillate flowers with 5 separate pistils at the base of the cup-shaped calyx and 15 nonfunctional, small stamens; staminate flowers larger, with 15 stamens.

Open woods; west of the Cascades from British Columbia to California. This is one of the first shrubs to blossom in early spring,

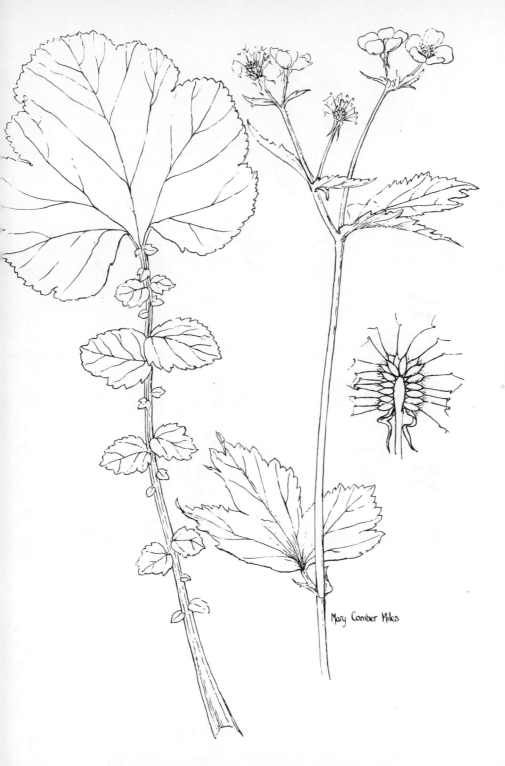

Large-leaved avens. *Geum macrophyllum*

male

female

male

female

Mary Comber Miles

Indian peach. *Osmaronia cerasiformis*

the blossoms appearing before the leaves are fully out. Broken stems have a pungent odor which helps to identify the shrub at any time of the year.

Ninebark, *Physocarpus capitatus* (Pursh) Kuntze
Erect spreading shrub up to 12 feet tall; bark brown, shredding in layers; leaves 1 1/2 to 3 1/2 inches long, oval to roundish, 3-lobed, toothed; flowers white, borne in rounded, terminal clusters; stamens many, red, as long as the petals.

Along streams, from central California to British Columbia and east to Montana.

Rose, *Rosa*

In this genus are all the wild roses, which are among our most beautiful roadside plants. There are four species in our area but these have become hybridized to such an extent that exact determination of species is difficult, many specimens bearing characteristics of two species.

The rose fruit, the hip, is rich in vitamin C, and it was used for food by the Indians when nothing else was available. In 1943 over 500 tons of rose hips were collected from the hedgerows of Britain and made into a syrup called National Rose Hip Syrup. It was estimated that the two and a half million bottles distributed had a vitamin C content equivalent to twenty-five million oranges.

The Indians boiled wild rose roots to make a shampoo for their hair. A tea was also made from the roots and used for sore eyes.

Key to Species

1 Prickles minute, hairlike; plants of the woods
                              Wood rose, *R. gymnocarpa*
1 Prickles larger, not hairlike; plants of the open
  2 Leaflets and flower stem glandular, spines stout
    3 Prickles sharply down-curved; foliage sweet-smelling
                              Sweetbrier, *R. rubiginosa*
    3 Prickles mostly straight; foliage not sweet-smelling
                              Common wild rose, *R. nutkana*
  2 Leaflets and flower stems not glandular; spines weak,
     straight   Clustered wild rose, *R. pisocarpa*

Wood rose, *Rosa gymnocarpa* Nutt.
Shrub with slender stems covered with minute, hairlike prickles;

leaves pinnately compound with 7 to 10 leaflets; leaflets oval, serrate, glandular on the margins; flowers pale pink, 1/2 to 1 inch
across, solitary or in twos; fruit oval, orange-red, the calyx lobes
falling off early.

Shady woods; British Columbia to Montana and California. This
species is the easiest to distinguish of the roses.

Common wild rose, *Rosa nutkana* Presl

Erect shrub, 2 to 6 feet tall; stems reddish, bearing stout,
straight prickles; leaflets 5 to 7, mostly 5, elliptic, toothed, glandular-hairy beneath; flowers mostly single or sometimes in twos
or threes, 1 1/2 to 3 inches across, pink; flower stems and calyx
with glandular hairs; hips globose, red, 1/2 to 3/4 inch long.

Open places; west of the Cascades from Alaska to northern California. The flowers of this rose are the largest and showiest of
our native species.

Clustered wild rose, *Rosa pisocarpa* Gray

Stems thin, with few, weak, straight prickles; leaves with 5 to
7 leaflets; leaflets not glandular, slightly hairy, oval, serrate;
flowers 3/4 to 1 inch across, pink to magenta, in clusters of 3 to
6; sepals long, ending in a broad leaflike tip, glandular; receptacle and flower stems not glandular; fruit globose, 1/4 to 3/8
inch long.

Open places; west of the Cascades from British Columbia to
northern California. This shrub is weaker than the common wild
rose, the flowers are smaller with a magenta coloring, and are
borne in clusters.

Sweetbrier, *Rosa rubiginosa* L.

Arching shrub; stems green, stout, with strong down-curving
prickles; leaves with 5 to 7 leaflets; leaflets oval, toothed, shining above, very glandular-hairy beneath and along the edges; flowers 1 to 4 in a cluster; sepals long-acuminate, often with small lateral leaflets, glandular; petals broad, pink to the middle, white toward the center; receptacle and flower stem glandular-hairy; hips
orange-red to red, pear-shaped.

Open areas; west of the Cascades from Washington to northern
California; naturalized from Europe. Sweetbrier is so named because the foliage has a sweet fragrance, especially noticeable in
the rain.

Rubus

The genus *Rubus* can be divided into 2 groups; those whose fruit can be removed from the receptacle like a cap, the raspberry, and those in which the receptacle breaks off with the fruit, the blackberry. However, since the fruit is often not available at flowering time, the key is constructed on vegetative and floral characters only.

Key to Species

1 Stems erect or semierect
  2 Flowers red   Salmonberry, *R. spectabilis*
  2 Flowers white
    3 Leaves compound; stems with a bluish, waxy coating
                                  Blackcap, *R. leucodermis*
    3 Leaves palmately lobed, not compound; stems not with a
      waxy coating   Thimbleberry, *R. parviflorus*
1 Stems arching or trailing, not erect
  4 Stems stout, ridged, bearing stout, broad-based recurving
      prickles
    5 Evergreen; leaflets deeply cut
                          Evergreen blackberry, *R. laciniatus*
    5 Deciduous; leaflets not cut
                            Himalaya berry, *R. thyrsanthus*
  4 Stems slender, round, bearing slender, small-based,
      straight or recurving prickles
                            Wild blackberry, *R. macropetalus*

Evergreen blackberry, *Rubus laciniatus* Willd.
    Stems red to purple, stout, trailing, with many large, flattened curved prickles; leaves with 3 to 5 leaflets; leaflets divided into slender segments, all margins deeply toothed; flowers white or pink.
    Escaped from cultivation and common in western Oregon and Washington. It is frequently found growing with *R. thyrsanthus* in open areas. Both of these blackberries begin blossoming in June and their fruits mature late in July or August. The wild blackberry, however, blossoms in May and fruits in June.

Blackcap, *Rubus leucodermis* Dougl.
    Shrub, erect or semierect; old stems with a bluish, waxy coating; leaves compound with 5 to 7 leaflets; leaflets ovate, sharp-

Wild blackberry. *Rubus macropetalus*

ly toothed, green and smooth above, white-hairy on the undersurface; flowers white; calyx longer than the petals.

Open areas; British Columbia to California and east to Wyoming. The fruit is sweet and highly prized for its palatibility.

Wild blackberry, *Rubus macropetalus* C. and S.

Stems trailing, slender, with numerous small, curved prickles; leaves with 3 to 5 leaflets, or leaves nearest the flower undivided; leaflets ovate, doubly toothed; stamens and pistils on separate plants; staminate flowers showy, 1 inch or more across; petals white, oval, 1/2 inch long; stamens many; pistillate flowers smaller; petals narrow; pistils many, on an enlarged receptacle.

Open areas; British Columbia and Idaho south along the coast to northern California. The berries of this plant are considered the most delicious of all the blackberries.

Thimbleberry, *Rubus parviflorus* Nutt.

Erect shrubby plant without prickles; leaves 3 to 7 inches broad, palmately 3- to 5-lobed, toothed, minutely soft-hairy on both surfaces; flowers 1 to 4 or 5 in a terminal cluster, white, 1 to 1 1/2 inches across; sepals 5, large and rounded; stamens and pistils many.

Moist open or wooded areas; southern Alaska to New Mexico and east to the Great Lakes. The large white flowers resemble delicate roses. The fruit is thin, red, flat and raspberrylike.

Salmonberry, *Rubus spectabilis* Pursh

Shrub with reddish-tan, shreddy bark and few prickles; leaves divided into 3 leaflets; leaflets ovate, often lobed, double-toothed, sharp-pointed; flowers magenta to pink, about 1 inch across; sepals 5, united at the base; petals 5; stamens and pistils many.

Along creeks and in moist places; west of the Cascades, Alaska to California. This is a very early blossoming shrub. The salmon-colored berries are raspberrylike and juicy, but relatively tasteless. The northwest Indians consumed the young sprouts in great quantities either raw or tied in bundles and steamed over hot rocks.

Himalaya berry, *Rubus thyrsanthus* Focke

Stems large, reddish purple, angled, trailing, with many large prickles; leaves compound with 5 leaflets, the upper 3 leaflets larger than the lower 2; all serrate; leaves near the flowers often with only 3 leaflets; flowers in clusters, white or pink.

Escaped from cultivation, origin unknown.

Thimbleberry. *Rubus parviflorus*

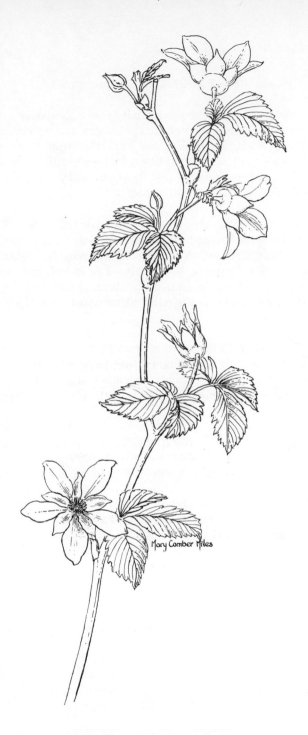

Salmonberry. *Rubus spectabilis*

PEA FAMILY, Leguminosae

Trees, shrubs, or herbs with alternate, usually compound leaves; stipules generally present; flowers irregular; sepals 5, partly united; petals 5, sometimes partly united, with one large upper petal (banner), 2 lateral ones (wings), and 2 lower (keel) enclosing the stamens and the pistil; stamens 10, usually with the filaments united; pistil 1; fruit a pod.

White-flowered broom, *Cytisus multiflorus* (Ait.) Sweet
    Bushy shrub; branches and stems dark green, angled, often nearly leafless; leaves very small with 3 narrow leaflets; flowers creamy white, 1 to 2 in the leaf axils, 1/4 to 3/8 inch long.
    White-flowered broom is an ornamental and can be seen in many gardens. It has escaped from cultivation and is abundant in a few localities.

Scotch broom, *Cytisus scoparius* (L.) Link
    Large bushy shrub, reaching 10 feet in height; stems angular, dark green; leaves small, usually with 3 leaflets, slightly hairy; flowers 7/8 inch long, bright yellow or yellow and red, pealike, in the leaf axils.
    Introduced as an ornamental from Europe, this species has become naturalized over a wide area. It is a very hardy plant and may be useful as a soil binder and soil renovator in some areas, or it may be somewhat of a weed by crowding out all competitive species.
    According to Dayton, *Important Western Browse Plants,* Scotch broom is poisonous to stock, producing symptoms of vomiting, staggering, and general paralysis.

Pea, *Lathyrus*

Key to Species

1 Flowers yellowish white   Yellow pea, *L. sulphureus*
1 Flowers bluish purple
    2 Leaflets elliptic; stipules narrow
                            Nuttall's pea, *L. nuttallii*
    2 Leaflets broadly oval; stipules broad, leaflike
                            Leafy pea, *L. polyphyllus*

Scotch broom. *Cytisus scoparius*

Nuttall's pea, *Lathyrus nuttallii* Wats.

Stems slender, angled; leaves with unbranched tendrils; leaflets 6 to 10, elliptic, acute at the apex; stipules narrow, sharp-pointed, flowers 2 to 6 in axillary racemes shorter than the leaves, bluish purple.

Open woods; western Washington and Oregon.

Leafy pea, *Lathyrus polyphyllus* Nutt.

Stems weakly erect, angled; leaflets 10 to 14, broadly oval, obtuse at the apex; stipules broad, leaflike, acuminate at the apex, heart-shaped at the base; flowers 3/4 inch long, 5 to 12 in a raceme shorter than the leaves, bluish purple.

Open woods; west of the Cascades from British Columbia to northern California.

Yellow pea, *Lathyrus sulphureus* Brew.

Stems stout, 1 to 3 feet tall; leaves with well-developed tendrils; leaflets 6 to 12, ovate to elliptic, obtuse at the apex with a short point; stipules large; flowers 5 to 10 or more in axillary racemes; petals yellowish white, becoming brownish with age.

Open woods; west of the Cascades from Washington to the Sierra Nevada, California.

Lupine, *Lupinus*

This is a large and difficult genus, and exact determination of species often requires the use of a hand lens. Many lupines have been proved poisonous, but experimental work has not been done on all species. Since differentiation of species is difficult, it is well to consider all lupines as potentially poisonous to animals.

Key to Species

1 Plants annual; 1 foot or less in height; flowers less than 1/4
      inch long   Small-flowered lupine, *L. micranthus*
1 Plants perennial; 1 to 3 1/2 feet tall; flowers 1/2 inch or
      more long
    2 Leaflets 10 to 17; keel without hairs
                                  Large lupine, *L. polyphyllus*
    2 Leaflets 5 to 9; keel hairy on the margin
      3 Hairs on the keel from the middle to the apex
                                  Riverbank lupine, *L. rivularis*

Leafy pea. *Lathyrus polyphyllus*

3 Hairs on the keel from the middle to the center of the flower
er
Broad-leaved lupine, *L. latifolius* var. *columbianus*

Broad-leaved lupine, *Lupinus latifolius* Agh. var. *columbianus* (Heller) C. P. Sm.

This species is found occasionally. The leaflets are 6 to 9, broadest toward the apex, sparsely hairy on the lower surface. The keel of the flower has hairs along the margin from the middle to the center of the flower.

Moist ground; western Oregon and Washington.

Small-flowered lupine, *Lupinus micranthus* Dougl.

Erect, branching annual, 6 to 13 inches tall; hairy throughout; leaves with 5 to 8 linear leaflets; petioles longer than the leaflets; flowers deep blue, in a raceme, the whorls of flowers widely spaced; flower stems very short; banner only slightly bent back, whole flower 3/16 to 1/4 inch long.

Dry ground; western Oregon to British Columbia and California. This is the first lupine to blossom in the spring. It is abundant along the dike of the Columbia River, growing in dry, sandy soil.

Large lupine, *Lupinus polyphyllus* Lindl.

Stout herb, 1 to 3 1/2 feet high, branching; lower leaves with long petioles, often over 1 foot long; leaves divided into 10 to 16 leaflets; leaflets widest above the middle, acute at the apex, tapering to the base, soft-hairy on both surfaces; flowers in a long raceme, pale bluish to white, becoming brown with age; banner sharply curled back in the open flowers; lateral petals broad, often with dark stripes, enclosing the keel; keel not hairy, white, with a black or deep blue tip, sharply curved upward; seed pods soft silky-hairy.

Open ground; west of the Cascades from British Columbia to California. This is the largest and showiest of the lupines.

Riverbank lupine, *Lupinus rivularis* Dougl.

Plants up to 3 feet high, branching; leaves with 5 to 9 linear leaflets, hairy on the undersurface, smooth above; petioles about as long as the leaflets; flowers lavender to purple with varying amounts of white; banner bent backward but not curled; keel hairy from the middle to the black tip.

Roadsides and moist sandy areas; from southern British Columbia through the Willamette Valley to California. This species and

Large lupine. *Lupinus polyphyllus*

the large lupine are the most common big lupines around Portland. The two can be distinguished by the larger size and greater number of leaflets in *L. polyphyllus*, and by the presence of hairs on the keel of *L. rivularis*.

Clover, *Trifolium*

The true clovers are herbs having compound leaves with mostly 3 leaflets. The flowers are borne in globose or elongated heads and are irregular. Many of the clovers are valuable as forage plants, soil enrichers, and bee plants. The species are not difficult to distinguish.

Key to Species

1 Heads red or crimson
  2 Heads elongated; stipules with rounded apex
                       Crimson clover, *T. incarnatum*
  2 Heads globose; stipules with sharp points
                       Red clover, *T. pratense*
1 Heads yellow, white, or pink
  3 Heads yellow, about 3/8 inch across
    4 Banner broad, heads 3/8 inch or more across
                       Hop clover, *T. procumbens*
    4 Banner narrow, heads generally 1/4 inch across
                       Small hop clover, *T. dubium*
  3 Heads white or pink; 1/2 inch or more across
    5 Plants creeping, rooting at the nodes; leaflets rounded
      or notched at the apex
                       White clover, *T. repens*
    5 Plants erect or spreading, not rooting at the nodes;
      leaflets with obtuse apex
                       Alsike clover, *T. hybridum*

Small hop clover, *Trifolium dubium* Sibth.
    Stems branching and spreading, about 6 inches in length; leaflets oval, rounded at the apex; heads 3/16 to 1/4 inch long, rounded; banner narrow, folded.
    Common lawn weed; introduced from Europe. This small hop clover may be distinguished from the larger hop clover, *T. procumbens*, by the smaller head and by the narrow, folded banner.

Red clover. *Trifolium pratense*

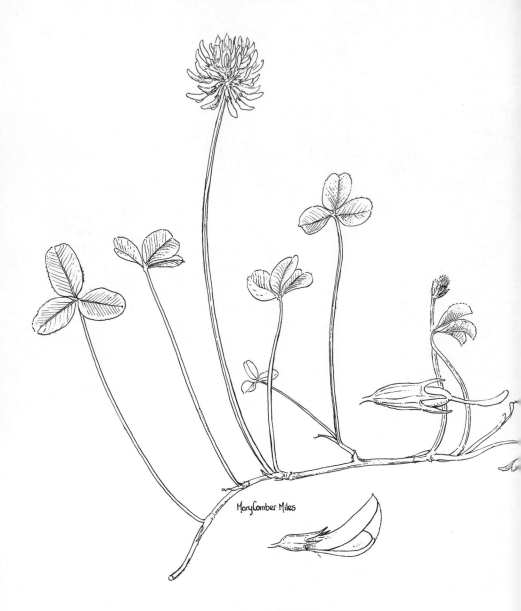

White clover. *Trifolium repens*

Alsike clover, *Trifolium hybridum* L.

Stems erect, branching, several from the base; leaves with 3 leaflets; leaflets 3/4 to 1 inch long, broadly oval, obtuse at the apex, tapering to the petiole, minutely toothed; flower heads globular, pink, borne on stems longer than the leaves.

Native of northern Europe. It is cultivated in the United States for hay, forage, seed, and as a soil enricher. It has established itself over a wide area, and it is common in fields and along roadsides. Alsike is a major honey plant producing honey of a white color and mild flavor.

Crimson clover, *Trifolium incarnatum* L.

Stems erect, 6 to 18 inches high, soft-hairy; leaflets broad at the top, tapering to the petiole, soft-hairy, minutely toothed; stipules large, rounded at the apex, dark-veined; heads elongated, reaching 2 inches in length; flowers crimson; calyx hairy.

This is a very showy clover, and a whole field in blossom is a spectacular sight. It was introduced from Europe as a crop and has escaped from cultivation in many areas. The honey produced from crimson clover is almost black in color.

Red clover, *Trifolium pratense* L.

Stems erect, branching, spreading, 1 to 2 feet tall; leaflets oval, obtuse at the apex, 3/4 to 2 inches long; stipules large, sharp-pointed, dark-veined; heads globular, red to purplish, with 2 sessile leaves immediately below.

Widely distributed. Red clover has long been cultivated as a crop plant, and it is found in fields and pastures throughout this country, Europe, and Asia.

Hop clover, *Trifolium procumbens* L.

Stems weak, branched, reaching 1 foot in length, slightly hairy; leaflets broad at the apex, rounded or notched; heads longer than broad, yellow, 3/8 inch long; flowers with broad, flattened banner.

Common in fields; introduced from Europe.

White clover, *Trifolium repens* L.

Stems creeping, rooting at the nodes; leaves with long petioles; leaflets broadly oval to round, often with a dent at the apex, finely toothed; heads borne on long stalks, much longer than the leaves; flowers white.

World-wide distribution in temperate regions. It is used for hay, green manure, pasture, and for enriching the soil. Because of its prostrate, spreading growth habit, white clover is the species most in demand in mixtures of lawn seed.

Both white clover and alsike clover often have a mark resembling a horse shoe in the center of each leaflet. These two clovers are grossly alike but alsike clover grows erect, not rooting at the nodes, whereas white clover is creeping and rooting at the nodes. The heads of white clover protrude much farther beyond the leaves than those of alsike.

White clover is one of several plants with 3 leaflets to which the name shamrock has been applied. Each is said to be the original plant picked by St. Patrick to symbolize the Trinity.

Vetch, *Vicia*

The genera *Vicia* and *Lathyrus* resemble each other very closely. The chief points of difference are the larger leaflets and weaker tendrils of *Lathyrus* and the fact that the style is hairy down the inner surface, while in *Vicia* the style has a tuft of hairs at the end like a cap.

Key to Species

1 Flowers in ones and twos in the leaf axils
   2 Leaflets widest above the middle
                       Common vetch, *V. sativa*
   2 Leaflets narrow, linear
                   Narrow-leaved vetch, *V. angustifolia*
1 Flowers in racemes in the leaf axils
   3 Flowers white or yellowish
      4 Plants stout; leaflets 16 to 30; flowers yellow-brown
                   Giant vetch, *V. gigantea*
      4 Plants slender; leaflets 8 to 20; flowers minute, white
                   Tare, *V. hirsuta*
   3 Flowers blue to purple
      5 Racemes dense, 1-sided; flowers deep purple
                   Hairy vetch, *V. villosa*
      5 Racemes 2- to 8-flowered, not 1-sided; flowers lavender
         to blue   Wild pea, *V. americana*

Wild pea, *Vicia americana* Muhl.
Stems weak, angled, often growing in a zigzag fashion; leaflets 7 to 12, broadly oval or elliptic, square or obtuse at the apex; stip-

ules deeply cut into 2 to 5 sharp points; flowers 2 to 8 in a raceme shorter than the leaves; petals purple to blue.

Open woods and waste lands; widely distributed in North America.

Narrow-leaved vetch or smaller common vetch, *Vicia angusti-folia* L.

Plants resembling *Vicia sativa*; leaflets narrow, square or pointed at the apex; flowers 1/2 inch long or less, narrow, purple.

Common; introduced from Europe and naturalized in Oregon and Washington. Between common vetch and narrow-leaved vetch there are all gradations of size, often making it difficult to decide with surety the species at hand.

Giant vetch, *Vicia gigantea* Hook.

Large plant, climbing; leaflets 16 to 28, narrow, 1 to 2 1/2 inches long; stipules large, entire or sharply cut; flowers yellowish brown, in racemes of 8 to 12, much shorter than the leaves.

Moist places; Willamette Valley and along the coast from Alaska to California.

Tare, *Vicia hirsuta* (L.) S. F. Gray

Stems weak, slender, angular, 1 to 2 feet in length; leaflets 12 to 18, narrow, square at the apex; stipules minute, branched; flowers 3 to 6 in a raceme, white to bluish, minute, on a stalk shorter than the leaves.

Introduced from Europe. It is found in fields and waste places, but it is much less common than the rest of the vetches.

Common vetch, *Vicia sativa* L.

Stems weakly erect, climbing by branching tendrils; leaflets 6 to 14, elliptic or linear, square or indented at the top, 1/2 to 1 1/8 inches long; stipules deeply sharp-toothed, sometimes much reduced; flowers 1 to 2 in the leaf axils, 1/2 to 1 inch long, purple and red.

Fields and roadsides; naturalized from Europe. This has long been in cultivation in the Northwest. In the cultivated state the leaflets are broad and the flowers large.

Hairy vetch, *Vicia villosa* Roth

Stems slender, weak, angled, soft-hairy; leaflets 10 to 20, long silky-hairy, narrow to elliptic, 1/4 to 1 inch long; flowers many in a dense 1-sided raceme, deep purple or banner blue and wing petals whitish, raceme longer than the leaves.

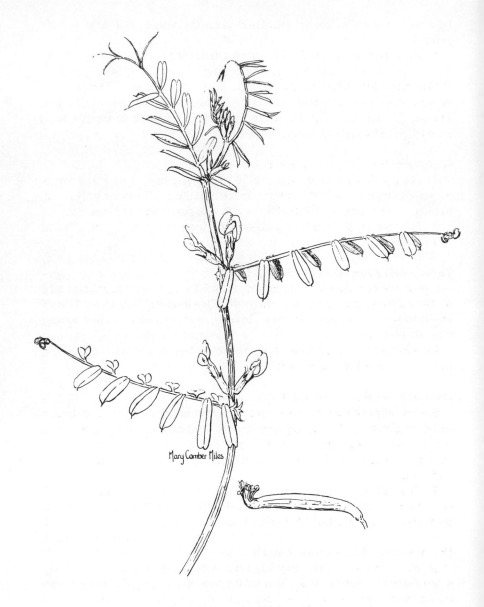

Common vetch. *Vicia sativa*

Common along roadsides and in fields. Introduced from Europe, it is grown as a seed crop in the Willamette Valley. Hairy vetch ranks with alsike clover as a honey plant of major importance.

WOOD SORREL FAMILY, Oxalidaceae

Key to Species of Oxalis

1 Flowers yellow
  2 Flowers bright yellow, leaves green
                            Yellow sorrel, *O. suksdorfii*
  2 Flowers pale yellow, leaves often purplish
                    Procumbent oxalis, *O. corniculata*
1 Flowers white
  3 Flowers solitary   Wood sorrel, *O. oregana*
  3 Flowers 2 to 5 at the end of the stem
            Many-flowered wood sorrel, *O. trilliifolia*

Procumbent oxalis, *Oxalis corniculata* L.
  This is an introduced species which is often found in gardens, lawns, and greenhouses. It differs from the yellow sorrel in having smaller and paler flowers, often with a red spot near the base of each petal, and leaflets frequently tinged with purple. It is a particularly troublesome weed since the stems root at the nodes, and in the process of cultivation the underground parts are not destroyed but remain alive, later sending up new plants.

Wood sorrel, *Oxalis oregana* Nutt.
  Plants with an underground rootstock; leaves divided into 3 rounded leaflets, notched at the apex and tapering at the base; flowers solitary, white, on a slender stalk bearing 2 bracts above the middle.
  Moist woods; western Washington to California.

Yellow sorrel, *Oxalis suksdorfii* Trel.
  Stems weakly erect from a slender rootstock; leaves alternate with 3 leaflets; leaflets green, heart-shaped, deeply notched at the apex; flowers yellow, solitary or in twos; flower stalks about as long as the leafstalks; petals 1/2 inch long or more, veined with red; stamens in 2 groups of 5; pistil with 5 styles.
  Common in open areas and in the woods; from Washington to California.

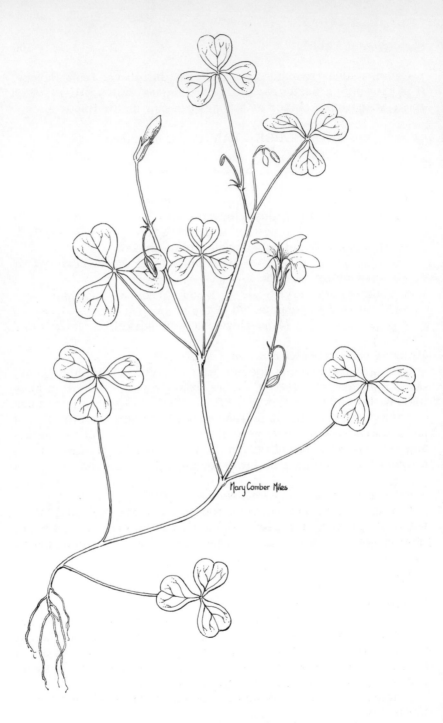

Yellow sorrel. *Oxalis suksdorfii*

Many-flowered wood sorrel, *Oxalis trilliifolia* Hook.

Flower stems reaching 10 inches in height; leaves long-stalked; flowers white to pinkish, 2 to 5 at the end of the stem.

Moist woods; western Washington and Oregon.

GERANIUM FAMILY, Geraniaceae

Herbs with lobed or cut leaves; flowers with 5 sepals, 5 petals, and 5 to 15 stamens; pistil with 5 styles, splitting at maturity into 5 separate, 1-seeded dry fruits.

Cut-leaved geranium, *Geranium dissectum* L.

Branched plant; leaves half-round or triangular in outline, divided deeply into 5 to 7 linear segments, these with 2 or 3 shallow lobes, hairy; flowers reddish purple, solitary or in twos in the leaf axils; calyx with sticky hairs; ovary lobes hairy, the surface netted and dotted but not wrinkled; seeds with a netted surface.

This is introduced from Europe and has become a common weed. A closely related species, *Geranium carolinianum* L. is also found in this area. It differs from the cut-leaved geranium in having light pink flowers, and the calyx is usually not sticky-hairy.

Dove's-foot geranium, *Geranium molle* L.

Plants weakly erect, branching; leaves round in outline, 5- to 9-parted, the lobes again 2- to 3-lobed, hairy; flowers purple, in twos in the leaf axils, the flower stem exceeding the length of the leaf; sepals 5, hairy, shorter than the petals; petals 5, notched; stamens 10, shorter than the petals; pistil with 5 stigmas; ovary 5-lobed, the lobes transversely wrinkled, not hairy. In fruit the style is thickened, forming a beak at the base of which are the 5 ovary lobes.

Common weed of both cultivated and waste lands; introduced from Europe. A hand lens is necessary for exact determinations in the genus *Geranium*. There are leaf differences, but these are difficult to observe without two different species for comparison. The most positive identification is based on the surface of the ovary lobes, whether it is smooth, wrinkled, hairy, or netted. Another important character is the presence or absence of sticky hairs (hairs with a glandular knob at the apex) on the calyx.

Filaree, *Erodium cicutarium* (L.) L'Her.

Stems low and spreading in early spring, becoming erect later;

Filaree. *Erodium cicutarium*

leaves opposite, unequal in size, hairy, finely dissected; flowers
rose-purple, in umbels of 2 to 8, extending beyond the leaves.

Common plant of dry ground; naturalized from southern Europe.
It is of value as forage for all kinds of livestock, but around Portland it is chiefly a garden and field weed.

SUMAC FAMILY, Anacardiaceae

Poison oak, *Rhus diversiloba* T. and G.

Shrub, low or up to 10 feet high, or becoming a tree-climbing
vine; leaves compound with 3 or occasionally 5 leaflets, new leaves
at first reddish, later becoming green; leaflets oval or ellip-
tical, wavy or lobed on the margins; flowers very small, greenish,
in panicles borne in the leaf axils.

Dry woods and roadsides; west of the Cascades from southern
British Columbia to southern California. The plant is toxic to
most individuals, producing an irritating skin rash. The foliage
is attractive both in early spring and in fall, and it is often unwit-
tingly gathered for decorating purposes. Bees visit the flowers and
gather both nectar and pollen. A white honey is produced which is
not poisonous.

BURNING BUSH FAMILY, Celastraceae

Western burning bush, *Euonymus occidentalis* Nutt.

Erect shrub 6 to 18 feet tall with slender, 4-angled branches;
leaves deciduous, opposite, ovate or widest above the middle,
minutely toothed, acute or acuminate at the apex; flowers brownish
purple, 1 to 5 on stalks in the leaf axils; petals 4 to 5, spreading,
below a conspicuous thick disk; stamens as many as the petals and
inserted on the disk.

Moist woods, not common; Washington and Oregon south to San-
ta Cruz County, California, and east to Nevada.

BUCKTHORN FAMILY, Rhamnaceae

Oregon tea or buckbrush, *Ceanothus sanguineus* Pursh

Shrub 3 to 10 feet tall with reddish brown stems; leaves alternate, ovate, finely toothed, with 3 main veins from the base; flowers 1/8 inch across, white, in dense clusters 2 to 4 inches long.

Open places; British Columbia to western Montana and south to
northern California. A distinctive characteristic of the shrub is
its heavy, musky odor. The plant has been used as a native sub-

stitute for oriental tea. The Indians used it as a medicine for tuberculosis. The leaves were also pounded into poultices for burns or to dry up sores. The Indian name for *Ceanothus sanguineus* is "Moon-num Moon-num."

MALLOW FAMILY, Malvaceae

Showy wild hollyhock, *Sidalcea virgata* Howell
Stems slender, erect, 10 to 36 inches tall; basal leaves with a long stalk, roundish in outline, cut into 5 to 7 toothed lobes; stem leaves smaller, deeply 3- to 7-lobed, all leaves with branched hairs; flowers deep pink, in a raceme; calyx 5-cleft; petals 5; stamens many, united in 2 tiers.

Dry open ground; Willamette Valley. This is a very showy roadside flower, common south of Salem and McMinnville, but scarce as far north as Portland. It blossoms in late April and May.

In June the tall wild hollyhock, *Sidalcea campestris*, is seen along the Willamette Valley roadsides. It can easily be distinguished from the showy hollyhock by the pale pink flowers and the gray-green appearance of the foliage.

VIOLET FAMILY, Violaceae

Violet, *Viola*

The genus is readily identified by the flower, which has the same general shape in all species. The two side petals are narrow, the two upper petals are erect, and the lowest petal is broad and usually spurred at the back. None of our native species is fragrant. The violet is the state flower of Illinois, New Jersey, Rhode Island, and Wisconsin.

Key to Species

1 Flowers yellow
   2 Leaves evergreen; stems creeping
                         Evergreen violet, *V. sempervirens*
   2 Leaves thin, deciduous; stems erect, leafy
                         Wood violet, *V. glabella*
1 Flowers blue   Howell's violet, *V. howellii*

Wood violet or Johnny-jump-up, *Viola glabella* Nutt.
Leaves and stem arising from an underground rootstock; stem

Mary Comber Miles

Wood violet or Johnny-jump-up. *Viola glabella*

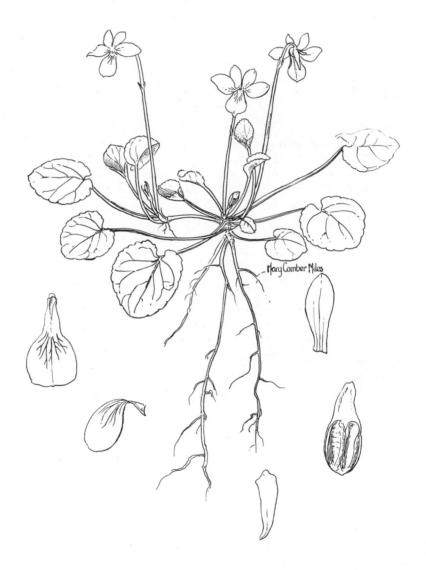

Evergreen violet. *Viola sempervirens*

with 2 or more leaves; leaves broad, heart-shaped at the base, sharp-pointed at the apex, toothed at the edges; flowers bright yellow with black lines on the lateral and lower petals.

Shady woods; west of the Cascades from southern Alaska to California. In March and April the wooded areas of Portland are a beautiful sight with this yellow violet and the white trillium in blossom together.

Howell's violet, *Viola howellii* Gray

Plants 2 to 8 inches tall; leaves round to broadly ovate in outline, cordate at the base, shallowly toothed on the margins; flowers blue, on stems longer than the leaves; lower petal with a short, broad spur.

Open hillsides and woods; west of the Cascades from British Columbia to southern Oregon.

Evergreen violet, *Viola sempervirens* Greene

Small plant with a creeping habit; leaves evergreen, heart-shaped at the base, rounded at the apex, shallowly toothed; old leaves with minute brown dots; petals pale yellow with reddish-brown lines.

In fir woods; west of the Cascades from British Columbia to California. The blossoms appear in early spring but are often missed because of their pale yellow color and low habit.

PARSLEY FAMILY, Umbelliferae

Herbs with alternate, usually compound leaves, the petioles often expanded at the base; flowers small, in umbels; sepals 5, completely or partly united; petals 5, attached with the 5 stamens to the disk around the top of the inferior ovary; fruit dry.

Poison hemlock, *Conium maculatum* L.

Stout plant 6 to 10 feet tall, much branched; stems hollow, green with purplish or red splotches; leaves with broad, sheathing petioles below, sessile above, pinnately 3 times divided; leaflets pinnately cut and deeply toothed; flowers in dense compound umbels, very small, white; calyx teeth absent; petals 5, turned inward; stamens 5, white.

Naturalized from Europe and well established around Portland and in the Pacific states. The whole plant has a nauseous odor, especially when bruised. This is one of the oldest known plant poisons, the fruit being the most poisonous part of the plant. The

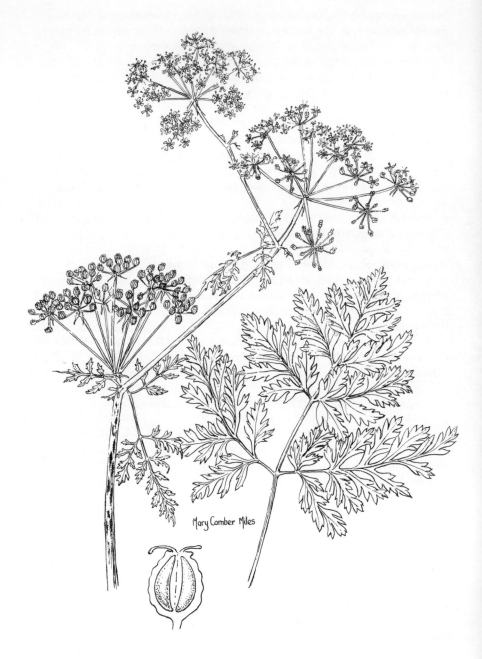

Poison hemlock. *Conium maculatum*

Greeks used it as a means of quick death to prisoners. It is probable that this was the hemlock given to Socrates.

Wild carrot or Queen Anne's lace, *Daucus carota* L.

Erect branching biennial arising from a carrotlike taproot; leaves lacy, pinnately compound, the leaflets pinnately divided into linear segments; flowers minute, white, in a flat-topped compound umbel, often with one or more reddish-purple flowers at the center of the inflorescence.

Introduced from Europe and now an abundant weed throughout the country. This is the wild form of our cultivated carrot. It generally blossoms in the middle of June.

Cow parsnip, *Heracleum lanatum* Michx.

Plants 4 to 8 feet tall; stems stout, hollow, ribbed, hairy; leaves 1 foot or more across, divided into 3 leaflets; leaflets lobed and toothed; leaf stem broadly sheathing at the base, hairy; flowers in flat, compound umbels, white, the outer petals larger than the others.

Moist ground; Alaska to California and across the continent. The flower stems and leafstalks are edible. Haskin in *Wild Flowers of the Pacific Coast* recommends that they be gathered just before the blossoms open. The stem should be peeled and cooked like rhubarb. When very soft and tender, the stems may be creamed and served, or they may be eaten raw in salads. All of the Indian tribes made use of this plant, eating it raw much as we do celery. Cattle also relish it and will eat it at every opportunity. The generic name comes from the Greek name for Hercules and suggest the great size of the plant.

Common sweet cicely, *Osmorhiza chilensis* H. and A.

Plants 10 to 24 inches tall, branching; leaves hairy, twice divided into threes; leaflets ovate, pointed at the apex, deeply and sharply toothed on the margins; petioles hairy, sheathing at the base; flowers minute, in a wide-spreading, compound umbel.

Shady woods; widely distributed in North America and also in Argentina and Chile.

Purple snakeroot, *Sanicula bipinnatifida* Dougl.

Stems erect, branching, 6 to 18 inches tall; leaves variable, mostly basal, 2 1/2 to 4 1/2 inches long, 5- to 9-parted, the divisions widely separated and again cleft or lobed, all lobes with marginal teeth; umbel with several branches, each ending in a compact head; flowers dark purple, some perfect and some staminate.

Open hillsides; west of the Cascades from Vancouver Island to California.

DOGWOOD FAMILY, Cornaceae

Creek dogwood, *Cornus pubescens* Nutt.

Shrub up to 15 feet high; young stems red or purplish; leaves 2 to 6 inches long, ovate to elliptic, entire or wavy on the margins, acute at the apex and base, short-hairy; flowers small, white, borne in terminal flat-topped clusters 1 1/2 to 3 inches across.

Moist thickets along streams; west of the Cascades from Washington to southern California.

HEATH FAMILY, Ericaceae

Trees, shrubs, or herbs with simple leaves; flowers urn-shaped, solitary or in clusters; sepals and petals 4 or 5; stamens as many, or twice as many, as the petals; ovary inferior or superior; fruit fleshy.

Salal, *Gaultheria shallon* Pursh

Evergreen shrub, mostly under 3 feet tall in this vicinity; stems red and hairy when young; leaves leathery, alternate, oval, pointed at the apex, rounded at the base, minutely toothed; flowers in a 1-sided raceme, pink or white, urn-shaped, glandular-hairy; bracts conspicuous, white to reddish.

Woods; west of the Cascades from Alaska to California. This shrub reaches its greatest size along the coast where it is frequently much higher than one's head. The purple-black fruits are good to eat and may be made into pies or used over shortcake. The Indians gathered salal fruits in great quantities. David Douglas hoped to introduce the plant into England as a commercial fruit. The shrub is now grown in that country as an ornamental, but the fruit has never been of commercial value either there or here. It is a source of nectar for bees.

Red huckleberry, *Vaccinium parvifolium* Sm.

Shrub 3 to 10 feet tall with angular green stems; leaves thin, oval, rounded at the apex and base, smooth on the margins; flowers greenish, urn-shaped, borne in the leaf axils; berries bright red.

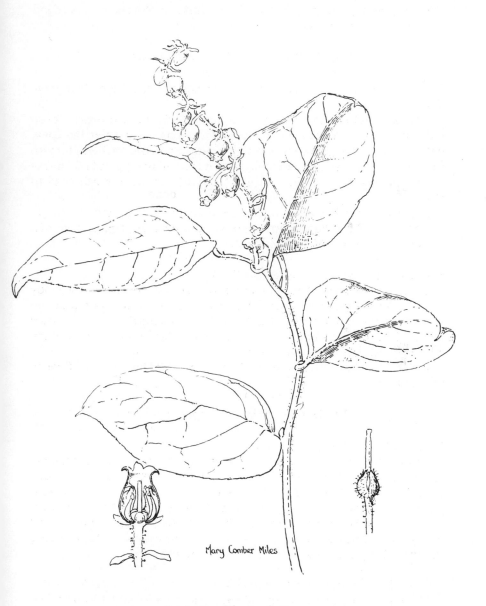

Mary Comber Miles

Salal. *Gaultheria shallon*

Wooded areas; west of the Cascades from Alaska to California. The huckleberry of importance to florists is the evergreen huckleberry, *Vaccinium ovatum* Pursh. It is common along the coast of Washington and Oregon, but in the vicinity of Portland it is found only as an ornamental.

PRIMROSE FAMILY, Primulaceae

Scarlet pimpernel or poor-man's-weatherglass, *Anagallis arvensis* L.

Low spreading annual with branches 2 to 12 inches long; leaves opposite, sessile, ovate, rounded at the base, acute at the apex, palmately veined; flowers scarlet to salmon-colored, solitary in the leaf axils on stalks extending beyond the leaves; petals 5, partly united; stamens 5, opposite the corolla lobes and attached to them.

Field and garden weed; introduced from Europe and sparingly established in the Willamette Valley and along the coast, common in central and southern California.

Starflower, *Trientalis latifolia* Hook.

Stem erect, about 4 to 6 inches tall, from an enlarged tuberous rootstock; leaves in a whorl of 3 to 6 (mostly 5) at the top of the stem, short-stalked, oval, tapering at both ends; flowers terminal; petals 5 to 7, united at the base, pink to white; stamens as many as the petals and opposite them.

Fir woods; Vancouver Island and western Washington and Oregon to California.

DOGBANE FAMILY, Apocynaceae

Periwinkle or creeping myrtle, *Vinca major* L.

Main stem trailing, rooting at the nodes; flower-bearing branches erect, 4 to 12 inches or more in height; leaves opposite, evergreen, shining, 3/4 to 3 1/2 inches in length, ovate, acute or acuminate at the apex, broadly rounded at the base; flowers deep blue, 1 to 1 1/2 inches long, borne singly in the leaf axils; petals united into a tube; sepals narrow, 1/4 to 1/2 inch long with hairs along the margins; stamens with anthers connected.

Lesser periwinkle, *Vinca minor* L.

Main stem trailing; flower-bearing branches erect, 4 to 8 inches high; leaves opposite, evergreen, elliptic to broadly lanceolate,

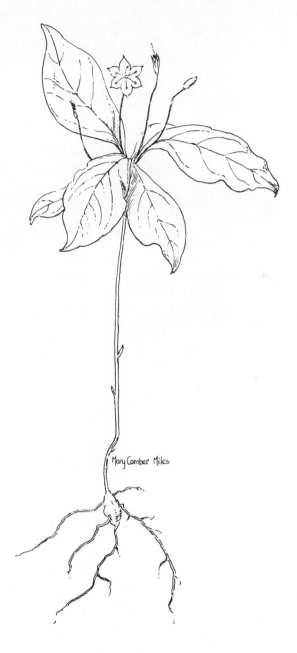

Starflower. *Trientalis latifolia*

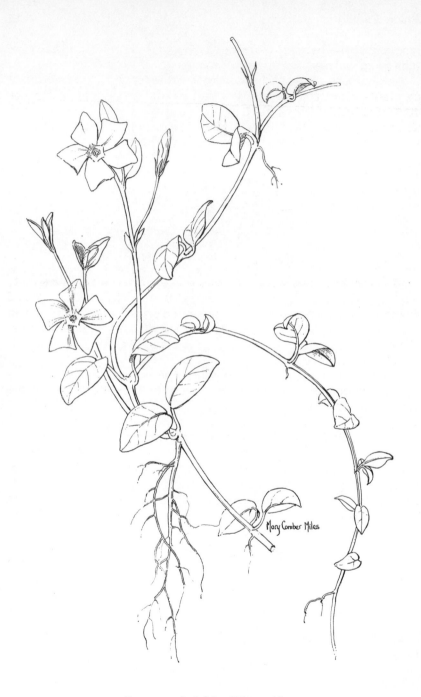

Lesser periwinkle. *Vinca minor*

tapering at the base; flowers deep blue, 3/4 inch long; sepals 1/8 inch long, without hairs; anthers united.

Both species of *Vinca* were introduced from Europe as cultivated plants, but are now well established here as escapes. The spreading habit makes the plants good ground cover for hillsides and other places where it is difficult to grow other plants. The two species may be distinguished by the leaf shapes, broadly ovate in *V. major*, elliptic in *V. minor,* and by the calyx, long, narrow, and hairy in *V. major,* and short and smooth in *V. minor*. The most common name for both plants is creeping myrtle, but this is misleading since the plants do not belong to the myrtle family.

PHLOX FAMILY, Polemoniaceae

Varileaved collomia, *Collomia heterophylla* Hook.
Herbs 4 to 20 inches tall, simple or branched, leafy throughout; leaves variable in shape, the lower pinnately divided with 3 to 5 segments, these 3- to 5-lobed, or the basal leaves lobed and toothed, and upper leaves entire or somewhat lobed; flowers pink, about 1/2 inch long, in clusters at the ends of branches; petals united, the lobes spreading.

In woods; west of the Cascades from Vancouver Island to California. This flower was first collected by David Douglas in the vicinity of Ft. Vancouver.

WATERLEAF FAMILY, Hydrophyllaceae

Herbs with hairy stems and leaves; leaves compound or divided; sepals 5, partly united, often with alternating down-turned appendages; petals 5, united at the base; stamens 5, attached to the base of the petals; pistil 1, compound; fruit a capsule.

Waterleaf, *Hydrophyllum tenuipes* Heller
Hairy herb, branching, erect, 12 to 18 inches tall; leaves with 3 leaflets; central leaflet 3-lobed, the lobes cut and toothed; lateral leaflets 2-lobed and toothed; flowers pale bluish to white or greenish, in a dense knoblike cluster; stamens 5, conspicuous, protruding well beyond the petals.

Moist woods; west of the Cascades from Washington to California.

Wood nemophila, *Nemophila parviflora* Dougl.
Weakly erect plant, 2 to 12 inches tall, branching from the base;

Mary Comber Miles

Waterleaf. *Hydrophyllum tenuipes*

leaves mostly opposite, deeply cut into 5 segments, the segments lobed or toothed; flowers 1/8 to 1/4 inch across, white or very light blue; sepals alternating with down-turned appendages.

Shade; western Washington and Oregon to California.

Small nemophila, *Nemophila pedunculata* Dougl.

Small spreading plant, 1 to 6 inches long; whole plant hairy; leaves opposite, mostly 5-parted, the segments sometimes lobed or toothed; flowers axillary; sepals 5, alternating with 5 down-turned appendages; petals 5, united at the base, pale bluish, 1/8 to 1/4 inch across.

Open ground and along roadsides; British Columbia to California, Idaho and Nevada.

BORAGE FAMILY, Boraginaceae

Western hound's-tongue, *Cynoglossum grande* Dougl.

Stout herb, 1 to 3 feet tall, generally hairy throughout; basal leaves long-ovate, 4 to 8 inches long, acute at the apex, tapering at the base to a long petiole; stem leaves smaller, ovate to lanceolate; flowers pink to bright blue, in a loose terminal panicle; petals spreading, each bearing 2 conspicuous white crests at the center.

Open ground or in woods; west of the Cascades from Washington to California. The name hound's-tongue refers to the shape of the leaf. This is an excellent garden plant, the bright flowers appearing in April and blossoming for a period of about two weeks.

Forget-me-not, *Myosotis*

Key to Species

1 Flowers yellow to blue; calyx hairs all hooked
>> Small blue forget-me-not, *M. versicolor*
1 Flowers blue with yellow centers; calyx hairs straight or hooked
> 2 Sepals united at the base for less than half their length; hairs of the calyx hooked toward the base
>> Garden forget-me-not, *M. sylvatica*
> 2 Sepals united at the base for more than half their length; hairs of the calyx all straight
>> True forget-me-not, *M. scorpioides*

Garden forget-me-not, *Myosotis sylvatica* Hoffm.

Stems 10 to 15 inches tall, slender or stout, usually branching, hairy; leaves oblong, obtuse at the apex; flowers in a long, 1-sided inflorescence, blue with yellow centers, 1/4 inch across; sepals narrow, united at the base for less than half their distance; hairs of the calyx slightly hooked toward the base of the calyx, straight on the lobes.

Common garden plant from Europe, naturalized locally in moist places. Another cultivated form, *Myosolis scorpioides* L., the true forget-me-not, occasionally becomes naturalized on wet soil. It also is blue with a yellow eye, but it may be identified by the character of the calyx. The united portion of the calyx is longer than the lobes, and the hairs are all straight and pressed closely to the calyx.

Small blue forget-me-not, *Myosotis versicolor* (Pers.) Sm.

Small hairy plant, 3 1/2 to 8 inches tall, erect, simple or branching; leaves linear, alternate; flowers minute, at first yellow, becoming blue, arranged in a coiled, 1-sided inflorescence; petals united into a tube at the base, the 5 lobes spreading abruptly, exposing the yellow-orange crests at the top of the petal tube; calyx with hooked hairs throughout.

Open fields, mostly west of the Cascades from Washington to California; naturalized from Europe. The name *Myosotis* is the Greek word for mouse ear, the name referring to the soft leaves of the plant.

Scorpion grass, *Plagiobothrys figuratus* (Piper) Johnst.

Slender erect herb, 4 to 18 inches tall, branched, hairy throughout; leaves without a petiole, linear, alternate above, opposite toward the base; flowers white with yellow centers, in a curved inflorescence; petals partly united, 5-lobed, bearing yellow crests at the center.

Open fields which are very wet in early spring; west of the Cascades from Vancouver Island to California. This species is abundant in the Willamette Valley where it produces the so-called "white lands" in May.

MINT FAMILY, Labiatae

Plants with 4-angled stems and opposite, simple leaves; flowers irregular, solitary or in clusters in the leaf axils; petals united,

2-lipped; stamens generally 4, attached to the corolla tube; ovary with 4 lobes, in fruit splitting into 4 nutlets.

Creeping Charlie or ground ivy, *Glecoma hederacea* L.

Main stems creeping, rooting at the nodes; flower-bearing stems erect, all stems 4-angled; leaves opposite, rounded, heart-shaped, coarsely toothed with rounded teeth; flowers irregular, 1 to 4 in the leaf axils, purple, on short leafstalks; petals 5, united; stamens 4, attached to the united petals.

Shady places; western Washington and Oregon to California, also in the North Atlantic states; naturalized from Europe. It is a fast-growing, herbaceous ground cover.

Red dead-nettle, *Lamium purpureum* L.

Plants erect, 3 to 18 inches tall; stems square, dark red; leaves opposite, heart-shaped, toothed, few below, crowded near the top of the stem, frequently purplish; flowers sessile in the upper leaf axils; petals purple, 5, united into a 2-lipped corolla.

Wet places; Washington to California; naturalized from Europe. Locally abundant, often taking over an entire field. Several such fields can be seen in the vicinity of Tigard, Oregon.

NIGHTSHADE FAMILY, Solanaceae

Small bittersweet, *Solanum dulcamara* L.

Climbing herbaceous vine; leaves alternate, broadly ovate, acuminate at the apex, simple, or deeply cut at the base into 2 to 4 segments; flowers on a lateral branch opposite a leaf; inflorescence angular; petals 5-lobed, deep-purple with 2 whitish-green spots at the base of each lobe, curved sharply back exposing the yellow anthers surrounding the pistil; berries bright red.

Shade places; Washington to California; native of Europe. The green berries are poisonous and have been used to poison dogs, but the ripe berries are harmless, and they are used by some housewives for making pies and sauces.

Black nightshade, *Solanum nigrum* L.

Spreading annual, 10 to 32 inches long with erect or weak branches, stems angled, green; leaves ovate, entire or irregularly angled, tapering to the petiole; flowers 3 to 10 in the leaf axils; petals white, becoming purplish with age, bent backward; fruit a black, glossy berry.

Waste places; introduced from Europe and occasional in western

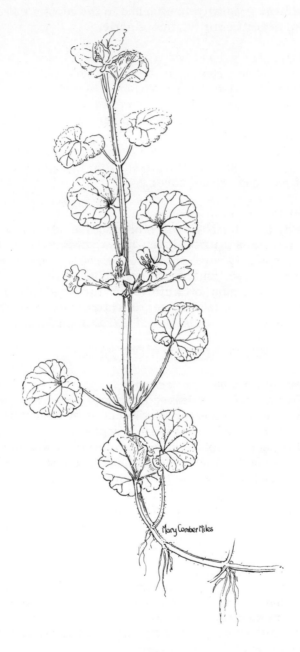

Creeping Charlie or ground ivy. *Glecoma hederacea*

and central Oregon. A common name often given to this plant is deadly nightshade, but it is doubtful if this plant can be fatal. The true deadly nightshade is a native of Europe and belongs to the genus *Atropa*.

FIGWORT FAMILY, Scrophulariaceae

Plants with simple leaves; flowers very slightly to definitely irregular; petals united at least at the base; stamens 2, 4, or 5, attached to the corolla; pistil 1, superior; fruit a capsule.

Large-flowered blue-eyed Mary, *Collinsia grandiflora* Dougl.
Plants 4 to 16 inches tall; upper leaves opposite or whorled, narrowly oblong to elliptic, obtuse at the apex, sessile; lower leaves shorter, oval, petioled, often with a few teeth on the margin; flowers 1 or more in the axils of the upper leaves; petals united forming a 2-lipped corolla; upper lip white with wide-spreading lobes; lateral lobes blue-violet, about the same length as the paler lower lobe.
Rocky moist ground; Vancouver Island to California. This is a very beautiful, showy wildflower, but it is not common around Portland.

Small-flowered blue-eyed Mary, *Collinsia parviflora* Dougl.
Plants weak, 2 to 16 inches tall; upper leaves sessile, narrow to oval, opposite or whorled toward the top, entire or few-toothed on the margins; lower leaves roundish, petioled; petals united forming a 2-lipped corolla; upper lip white; lateral lobes blue-violet, longer than the middle lobe.
Moist soil; British Columbia to southern California, east to Ontario, Michigan and Colorado.

Monkey Flower, *Mimulus*

Key to Species

1 Plants slimy-hairy at least below; leaves pinnately veined
                            Musk flower, *M. moschatus*
1 Plants not slimy; leaves palmately veined
    2 Flowers less than 1/2 inch long, with one purplish-red spot
        on the lower lip
                        Chickweed monkey flower, *M. alisnoides*

Common monkey flower. *Mimulus guttatus*

2 Flowers 1 inch or more long, bearing many brownish-red
     dots in the corolla tube
                         Common monkey flower, *M. guttatus*

Chickweed monkey flower, *Mimulus alisnoides* Dougl.

Weakly erect annual, 2 to 12 inches tall, simple or branched;
leaves ovate, toothed, palmately veined, tapering to a flat petiole;
flowers yellow, less than 1/2 inch long; petals united into a tube
with 2 divisions above and 3 below, the lower lip with a reddish-
purple dot in the center.

On wet rocks or banks; from Vancouver Island to northern California.

Common monkey flower, *Mimulus guttatus* DC.

Stems erect, angled, reaching 3 feet in height in shady locations;
leaves broadly ovate or roundish, irregularly toothed; lower leaves
with stalks, the upper leaves sessile, becoming smaller toward the
top of the stem; flowers deep yellow, 1 to 1 1/2 inches long, with
brownish-red dots in the corolla tube; calyx 5-parted with 5 prominent ridges.

Along streams; British Columbia and Montana to Mexico. The
name comes from the fact that the petals together are supposed to
resemble a monkey face, but this resemblance is difficult to see.

Musk flower, *Mimulus moschatus* Dougl.

Slender weak plant, 6 to 12 inches tall, slimy-hairy at least on
the lower parts; leaves thin, narrowly oblong to ovate, toothed,
pinnately veined, acute or obtuse at the apex; flowers usually less
than 1 inch long, light yellow, hairy, corolla lobes rounded, spreading.

Along streams and in bogs; British Columbia and Montana south
to southern California, Utah, and Colorado; also in northeastern
North America. The musk flower was introduced into England by
David Douglas, who discovered it near the Columbia River in Washington. The plant became a favorite in English flower gardens because of its musklike odor. However, after a number of years in
cultivation, it lost its odor and its popularity. No explanation has
been offered for the loss of the scent. Even in its native habitat
the musk flower is not always scented.

California figwort, *Scrophularia californica* C. and S.

Stout, erect plant 2 to 5 feet tall; leaves opposite, oval to broadly
ovate, heart-shaped or square at the base, pointed at the apex,

toothed on the margins; flowers in a large spreading panicle, irregular, reddish brown, 1/4 to 1/2 inch long.

Moist places in the open; western Washington, Oregon, and California.

Spring queen, *Synthyris reniformis* Benth.

Flower stems and leaves arising from an underground rootstock; leaves rounded to heart-shaped, scalloped at the edges, palmately veined, often reddish purple on the underside; flowers in racemes about as long as the leaves, blue-lavender; stamens longer than the petals.

Moist woods; west of the Cascades from California to Washington. This plant is not common around Portland but may be found occasionally. It is one of the first herbs to blossom in the spring, and is excellent for border plantings.

Speedwell, *Veronica*

Key to Species

1 Flowers in racemes; plants growing in streams or very wet
     places
  2 Leaves ovate to oblong, short-petioled
                                    American speedwell, *V. americana*
  2 Leaves long, narrow, without petioles
                              Narrow-leaved speedwell, *V. scutellata*
1 Flowers solitary in the leaf axils; plants not growing in very
     wet places
  3 Flowers pale blue to white, on very short stalks
                                        Small speedwell, *V. arvensis*
  3 Flowers bright blue, on stalks longer than the leaves
                                      Winter speedwell, *V. persica*

Common or American speedwell, *Veronica americana* (Raf.) Schwein.

Weakly erect plant sometimes reaching 3 feet in length, often rooting at the lower nodes; leaves opposite, all petioled, oblong to ovate, toothed along the margins; flowers in racemes in the leaf axils, the racemes longer than the leaves; petals bright blue with white at the center, lined with dark blue or purple.

Very wet ground or in slow-moving streams; Alaska to California and across the continent.

Common or American speedwell. *Veronica americana*

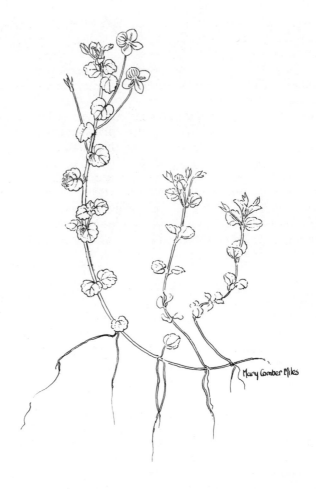

Winter speedwell. *Veronica persica*

Small speedwell, *Veronica arvensis* L.

Stems branched, spreading, mostly 3 to 10 inches tall; lower leaves opposite, stalked, oval and toothed; upper leaves becoming alternate, sessile, linear and smooth on the margins; all leaves with more than one vein from the base; flowers about 3/8 inch long, white to blue, solitary in the upper leaf axils on very short stalks; petals 4, slightly united at the base, often with 5 or 6 dark lines; stamens 2 with purple anthers; ovary flattened and notched.

A native of Europe; this species is widespread both in gardens and in waste places.

Winter speedwell, *Veronica persica* Poir.

Plants weakly erect, branching or simple, 2 to 8 inches tall; leaves alternate or opposite or both, round or broadly ovate in outline, toothed; flowers blue, in the leaf axils on stalks much longer than the leaves; petals 4, dark-lined, united at the base, one petal smaller and lighter blue than the other 3.

Common lawn weed; introduced from Europe and common in the Willamette Valley. Frequently in early spring many lawns in Portland appear blue with the blossoms of this plant.

Narrow-leaved speedwell, *Veronica scutellata* L.

Stems slender, weak, 3 to 16 inches long, simple or somewhat branched; leaves long and narrow, without stalks; flowers in axillary racemes as long as the leaves; petals blue.

Swampy ground; British Columbia to central California and east across the continent; also in the Old World.

BROOMRAPE FAMILY, Orobanchaceae

Naked broomrape, *Orobanche uniflora* L.

Parasitic plant without green color, 3 to 8 inches tall, with an underground stem and erect flower stalks; leaves reduced to scales; flowers irregular, purplish or sometimes yellowish; sepals 5, united; petals 5, united into a 2-lipped, curved tube; stamens 4, attached to the corolla tube.

Parasitic on several different plants; from British Columbia to California and the eastern states. The plant is rather rare but a spectacular display of this species can be seen on the rocky hillside along the highway at Carrolls, Washington, where it is parasitic on *Sedum*.

Another species of *Orobanche, O. fasciculata,* has been found near Troutdale, Oregon, growing in a carrot field and on the red clover adjoining the field.

PLANTAIN FAMILY, Plantaginaceae

English plantain, *Plantago lanceolata* L.

Flower stems 6 to 24 inches high, arising from a rosette of basal leaves; leaves long-linear, hairy, with 3 to 5 conspicuous parallel ribs; flowers in a dense brownish spike, chaffy, stamens protruding 1/4 to 1/2 inch from the flower.

This is a common lawn weed; west of the Cascades and across the continent; introduced from Europe. It is a favorite of children, who wrap the stem around the base of the spike and shoot it off for a considerable distance.

Broadleaf plantain, *Plantago major* L.

Leaves all basal; flower stems 2 to 12 inches high; leaves broadly spade-shaped or elliptic, the conspicuous ribs following the contours of the leaf, soft-hairy; flowers in elongated, chaffy spikes.

Like English plantain this is a well-known introduced weed which has spread throughout North America. According to Jepson, "it is called 'White Man's Foot,' since it has closely followed the advance of civilization, springing up about the earliest frontier settlements."

The venation in these two species is netted, but the main ribs run parallel.

MADDER FAMILY, Rubiaceae

Bedstraw, *Galium*

Key to Species

1 Leaves narrow, linear, 1 to 1 1/2 inches long
                                   Cleavers, *G. aparine*
1 Leaves oblong, less than 1 inch long
    2 Plants fragrant, flowers in axillary groups of 3
                                   Fragrant bedstraw, *G. triflorum*
    2 Plants not fragrant, flowers in large terminal clusters
                                   Wild madder, *G. mollugo*

Cleavers, goose grass, or bedstraw, *Galium aparine* L.

Stems weak, trailing over other herbs, 4-angled; leaves in

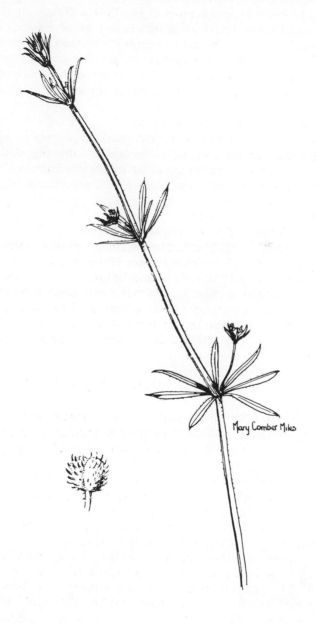

Cleavers, goose grass, or bedstraw. *Galium aparine*

whorls of 6 to 8, long-linear, with stiff hairs; flowers 1 or 2 in the leaf axils; fruit with stiff, hooked hairs.

Grassy fields throughout most of the United States. In the summer the small round fruits stick tightly to hikers' clothing by their hooked hairs and well deserve another common name, beggarticks. Many European writers state that the seeds of cleavers make a good coffee substitute. This is not hard to believe since cultivated coffee and cleavers belong to the same family.

Wild madder, *Galium mollugo* L.

Plants with stems 1 to 3 feet long, smooth; leaves in whorls of 6 to 8, oblong, sharp-pointed at the apex, tapering at the base; flowers white, many, in terminal or axillary clusters.

Introduced from Europe; sparingly established in the Willamette Valley.

Fragrant bedstraw, *Galium triflorum* Michx.

Stems 4-angled, weakly erect or reclining; leaves in whorls of 6, oblong, pointed at the apex and base; flowers greenish white, in the leaf axils, usually in threes and borne on a stalk as long as, or longer than, the leaves; fruits with white hooked hairs.

Open areas throughout the United States. The whole plant has a sweet, delicate fragrance. To the naked eye the fruits look like small fuzzy balls, but with a lens one can see the hook on the end of each hair.

HONEYSUCKLE FAMILY, Caprifoliaceae

Erect or climbing woody plants with opposite leaves; flowers regular or irregular; petals generally 5, united; stamens usually 5, attached to the corolla; ovary inferior; fruit fleshy or dry.

Twinflower, *Linnaea borealis* L. var. *americana* (Forbes) Rehd.

Stems trailing, slender; leaves evergreen, opposite, oval, serrate above the middle; flower-bearing stems erect; flowers in pairs at the ends of the branches, nodding, pink, bell-shaped; calyx linear, about 1/3 the length of the corolla.

Moist woods; western North America. Large masses of this plant may be seen in Hoyt Park and along Germantown Road in Portland. The generic name honors Linnaeus, the Swedish botanist. In pictures he is often shown holding the twinflower in his hand.

Climbing honeysuckle, *Lonicera ciliosa* (Pursh) Poir.

Stems woody, twining; leaves opposite, oval, obtuse at the apex, tapering to the petiole; leaves below the flowers united around the stem; flowers orange, in a close cluster; petals forming a tube 1 inch or more in length.

Climbing over other shrubs and trees in open woods; British Columbia and Montana to California. The flowers are abundant producers of nectar, but the honey bees cannot reach it.

Twinberry or bush honeysuckle, *Lonicera involucrata* Banks

Bush 4 to 7 feet tall with light tan bark; leaves opposite, elliptic, pointed at the apex, tapering at the base, short-hairy on the under surface and along the margins; flowers yellow, in pairs in the leaf axils, surrounded by large broad bracts which become red with age; petals united into a tube with a saclike projection at the base; anthers projecting slightly from the corolla tube.

Moist thickets; Alaska to California and east to the Great Lakes. Not common, but it can be seen along the edges of open woods near Tigard. The fruit, sometimes called bearberry, was eaten by the Indians.

Blue elderberry, *Sambucus caerulea* Raf.

Large shrub or small tree; leaves opposite, pinnately compound with 5 to 9 leaflets; leaflets broadly linear, sharp-pointed, toothed; flowers white, 1/8 inch across, in wide-spreading, flat-topped clusters; fruit a blue berry.

Common in open areas; Washington to California, Montana, and New Mexico. The fruit is edible and makes good jelly and pies.

Red elderberry, *Sambucus callicarpa* Greene

This plant resembles the blue elderberry in vegetative characters, but it differs in having the white flowers borne in an elongated dome-shaped cluster and in having red berries. In Portland and in the Willamette Valley the flowers appear in June, whereas the flowers of blue elderberry are in blossom in April and May.

Open ground and woods; west of the Cascades, British Columbia to California. The generic name comes from the Greek, *Sambuke,* a triangular stringed instrument made from elderberry wood.

Western wayfaring tree, *Viburnum ellipticum* Hook.

Branched shrub up to 12 feet tall; leaves 1 1/2 to 3 inches long, oval to almost round, toothed above the middle, dark green above,

Red elderberry. *Sambucus callicarpa*

light green and sparsely hairy beneath; flowers white, in terminal cluster, 1 1/2 to 2 1/2 inches across.

Open woods and stream banks; west of the Cascades from Washington to California.

VALERIAN FAMILY, Valerianaceae

Corn salad, *Valerianella congesta* Lindl.

Erect plant with angled stems, simple or sometimes branched; leaves opposite and basal, oblong, rounded at the apex, sessile on the stem, petioled at the base of the plant; flowers pink, tubular, in dense heads.

Moist places; west of the Cascades from British Columbia to California. This is one of our most beautiful native wildflowers. Dense masses of corn salad mixed with large-flowered blue-eyed Mary cover the rocky hillside at Carrolls, near Longview, Washington.

Blue-flowered corn salad, *Valerianella locusta* (L.) Betcke

Plants with angular stems, 3 to 9 inches tall, branching regularly in twos; leaves opposite, elongated, rounded at the tips, sessile; flowers in heads in pairs at the ends of the branches, the upper leaves extending beyond the groups of flowers; flowers very small, bluish, tubular.

The name is derived from the fact that this plant has been cultivated for salad in its native southern Europe. It is not common around Portland but it may be found occasionally in cultivated fields or in open woods west of the Cascades.

GOURD FAMILY, Cucurbitaceae

Wild cucumber or old-man-in-the-ground, *Echinocystis oregana* Cogn.

Long-trailing vine with tendrils; leaves palmately 5- to 7-lobed; stamens and pistils in different flowers on the same plant; staminate flowers white, in long axillary racemes; stamens united; pistillate flower solitary, located in the same leaf axil as the staminate raceme. The vine grows from an enormous root as large as a man's body.

Common west of the Cascades from British Columbia to California. The name *Echinocystis* comes from the Greek *echinos*, a hedgehog, and *kystis*, a bladder, from the prickly fruit.

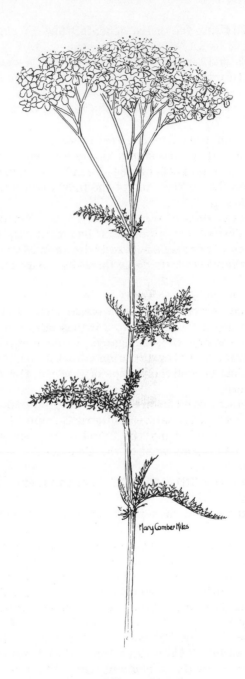

Yarrow. *Achillea millefolium*

COMPOSITE OR SUNFLOWER FAMILY, Compositae

Plants of this family have the flowers in a head surrounded by an involucre (one or many rows of bracts) and the flowers are either strap-shaped or tubular (fig. 12). The strap-shaped flowers are called ray flowers and occur at the margin of the head or throughout. The tubular flowers, called disk flowers, compose the disk of the head or they may occur throughout. The calyx, called pappus in this family, is either absent or modified in the form of bristles, hairs, scales, or teeth. The ovary is always inferior and the fruit is dry, containing a single seed. This is an immense family consisting chiefly of herbs.

Yarrow, *Achillea millefolium* L.

Stems erect, 1 to 3 feet high; unbranched; leaves alternate, pinnately divided into many fine segments giving a lacelike appearance; heads many, small, white, arranged in flat-topped clusters.

Common in open ground; west of the Cascades; introduced from Europe. The genus is named for Achilles, who is said to have used this plant to heal the wounds of his soldiers in the siege of Troy.

Corn chamomile, *Anthemis arvensis* L.

This plant resembles dog fennel except that there is no disagreeable odor and the entire plant is larger.

Cultivated ground; less common than dog fennel and readily distinguished from it by the lack of odor.

Dog fennel, *Anthemis cotula* L.

Plant 2 to 24 inches tall, branching, each branch terminating in a single head; leaves twice pinnately divided into many narrow segments; heads daisylike with 12 to 15 white flowers and yellow disk flowers; whole plant with a disagreeable odor.

Common in open fields and cultivated ground; introduced from Europe.

European daisy, *Bellis perennis* L.

Leaves all basal, rounded at the apex, tapering to a broad petiole, 1 to 1 1/2 inches long, shallow-toothed on the margin; heads solitary, daisylike, with white or pinkish ray flowers and yellow disk flowers.

Common in lawns throughout Portland and western Oregon; introduced from Europe. The generic name *Bellis*, daisy, probably comes from the Latin *bellus*, beautiful.

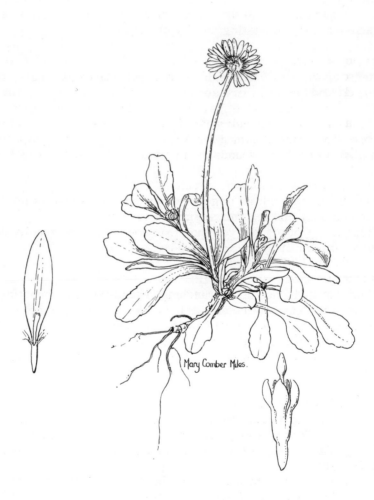

European daisy. *Bellis perennis*

Bachelor's-button or cornflower, *Centaurea cyanus* L.

Branched plants about 2 feet high, hairy throughout, often cottony; stem leaves alternate, narrow; basal leaves pinnately lobed, but withered and gone by the time blossoms appear; heads blue, purple, red, pink, or white, the outer tube flowers enlarged, irregular, sterile; bracts at the base of the head in several rows, fringed and either black or red on the edges.

Bachelor's-button is a common plant of fields and roadsides, blossoming from June throughout the summer. Apparently of south European or west Asiatic origin, it has spread over most of Europe and Asia as a cornfield weed, and is widely distributed in America. The generic name comes from centaur, because the centaur, Chiron, is said to have cured his wound with this plant when he was injured by an arrow shot by Hercules. Bees gather both nectar and pollen from bachelor's-button, but the honey produced is dark and strong-flavored.

Oxeye daisy, *Chrysanthemum leucanthemum* L.

Stems erect, 6 to 24 inches high, simple or branched; lower leaves spatula-shaped, tapering to a petiole, ragged-toothed or lobed; upper leaves linear, sessile; heads 1 1/2 to 2 inches wide, solitary at the end of the branches; ray flowers white, disk flowers yellow.

Common in open ground; widely distributed; native of Europe.

False dandelion or cat's-ear, *Hypochaeris radicata* L.

Leaves all basal, spreading, long-tapering with irregular rounded or sharp lobes, rough-hairy on both surfaces; flower stems branched, smooth, bearing few to many small bracts; flower heads yellow with several rows of erect green bracts at the base.

Lawn weed; western Oregon; introduced from Europe. This plant looks very much like the common dandelion, and in many places it is more abundant. It can be distinguished by its longer, branching flower stems, and by the presence of small bracts on the flower stems. Another character is the erect bracts at the base of the head of this species in contrast to the row of downward-turned bracts on the common dandelion.

In our area *Hypochaeris* is frequently attacked by gall midges, which stimulate the flower stem to produce swollen areas. Such swellings are not found on either the common dandelion or on hawkbit.

Oxeye daisy. *Chrysanthemum leucanthemum*

Pineapple weed. *Matricaria matricarioides*

Sweet coltsfoot. *Petasites frigidus*

Hawkbit, *Leontodon nudicaulis* (**L.**) Banks

Leaves forming a basal rosette, long-tapering with shallow or deeply-cut lobes, hairy on both surfaces; flower stem unbranched, solid, usually with hairs; heads yellow, with a single row of green bracts at the base; outer flowers of the head longer than the others.

Lawn weed; west of the Cascades, Vancouver Island to California; introduced from Europe. This plant resembles the common dandelion but it is found less often than either the common dandelion or the false dandelion. Like the false dandelion, it blossoms in June and throughout the summer.

Pineapple weed, *Matricaria matricarioides* (Less.) Porter

Erect, branching herb, 2 to 10 inches tall; leaves 2 or 3 times pinnately divided into narrow segments; heads dome-shaped, greenish yellow, with disk flowers only; bracts erect with papery margins.

Common in gardens and waste places from coast to coast and in Europe. The plant has a distinct odor described as pineapplelike.

Sweet coltsfoot, *Petasites frigidus* (**L.**) Fries var. *palmatus* (Ait.) Cronq.

Flower stalks stout, from an underground rootstock, bearing alternate scalelike leaves; basal leaves arising from the rootstock after the flowers are in full blossom, palmately 7- to 9-lobed, toothed, white-hairy on the under surface; flowers white to lavender, in cylindrical heads about 1/2 inch long; some heads containing mostly ray flowers with 1 or 2 disk flowers in the center, other heads with mostly disk flowers.

Shady, moist, wooded areas; west of the Cascades, British Columbia to California. The generic name is derived from the Greek, *petasos*, meaning broad-brimmed hat, from the shape of the basal leaves.

Common groundsel, *Senecio vulgaris* L.

Stems erect, branching; leaves alternate, sessile, narrow, pinnately cut, the margins jagged; heads in terminal groups; flowers all tubular, yellow, in cylindrical heads; bracts at the base of the head black-tipped, in one row with several very small bracts at the base.

Very common garden weed in western Oregon; native of Europe.

Common dandelion, *Taraxacum officinale* L.

Leaves spreading, all at the base of the plant, pinnately parted,

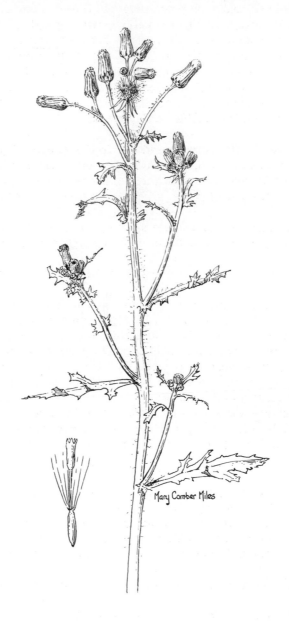

Common groundsel. *Senecio vulgaris*

Common dandelion. *Taraxacum officinale*

the segments triangular and ragged-toothed; flower heads solitary
on hollow stems arising from the center of the leaves; flowers all
strap-shaped, bright yellow; bracts at the base of the head in two
series, the upper erect, the lower turned downward.

Common everywhere; introduced from Europe. Common dandelion begins blossoming in about February or March, much ear-
lier than the other dandelionlike plants. The leaves are used both
here and in Europe as a cooked vegetable or as a salad.

Meadow or yellow salsify, *Tragopogon pratensis* L.

This species is very similar to the oyster plant, except that the
flowers are yellow.

Salsify or oyster plant, *Tragopogon porrifolius* L.

Stout herb with alternate grasslike leaves, sheathing at the base;
heads purple, large, solitary on long stalks, the stalk thickened
and hollow below the head; heads opening in the morning, closing
by noon; bracts at the base of the head in a single row, long-pointed.

Both purple- and yellow-flowered salsify are cultivated in Europe for the root, which is eaten as a winter vegetable. In the wild
state the root is smaller, but some people prefer the root of the
wild yellow salsify to the cultivated form. The base of the stem
and the lower leaves are also good as a cooked vegetable.

Both species are common in waste lands west of the Cascades
and across the continent.

Glossary

Acuminate. Tapering to a slender point.

Acute. Distinctly and sharply pointed, but not tapering.

Annual. A plant which completes its life history and dies within a year.

Anther. That portion of the stamen which contains the pollen.

Axil. The angle formed by the axis and any organ which arises from it, like the angle formed by a leaf or branch with the stem.

Axillary. Borne in an axil.

Axis. A central support.

Banner. The upper and largest petal of flowers of the pea family.

Basal. Situated at the base.

Berry. A fleshy or pulpy fruit with one or more seeds embedded in the pulpy tissue, as the grape, date, or tomato.

Biennial. Of two years' duration. A plant which completes its life history and dies within two years.

Bloom. A usually waxy, whitish or bluish powder covering the surface of a leaf, stem, fruit, or other organ.

Bract. A modified leaf below a flower.

Bulb. A shortened, mostly underground stem bearing fleshy leaves which contain stored food and water.

Calyx. The outer series of floral leaves; all the sepals together.

Capsule. A dry seed pod that opens to discharge its seeds.

Cleft. Cut about halfway to the midrib or base.

Compound. Composed of two or more similar parts united into one whole.

Cordate. Shaped like a heart.

Corolla. The petals of a flower collectively, either free or united.

Crest. A ridge or projection.

Cyme. A flower cluster in which the central flower blossoms first.

Deciduous. Falling in season, as petals fall after flowering, or as leaves do in the autumn.

Disk flower. One of the flowers in the central portion of a composite flower head.

Divided. Cut nearly to the base or to the midrib.

Entire. Without toothing or divisions; with even margin.

Exserted. Projecting.

Filament. The stalklike portion of a stamen bearing the anther.

Free. Unattached to other structures.

Fruit. A ripened ovary, together with any other parts which may develop with it.

Genus. A group of related species or, sometimes, a single species.

Gland. A secreting organ. A gland may be at the tip of a hair, on the surface of a leaf or stem, or embedded in tissue.

Glandular. Having or pertaining to glands.

Globose. Nearly spherical.

Habit. The general appearance of a plant.

Head. A cluster of sessile or essentially sessile flowers at the apex of a peduncle.

Herb. A nonwoody plant, at least one which is not woody above ground level.

Herbaceous. Not woody, having the characters of an herb.

Inferior. Lower or below some other organ.

Inflorescence. The flowering part of a plant, and the manner of its arrangement.

Involucre. A series of bracts surrounding or supporting a flower cluster, as in the heads of the composites or in the umbels of *Umbelliferae.*

Irregular. Asymmetric, as a flower which cannot be halved by any plane, or one which can be bisected in one plane only.

Keel. A prominent longitudinal ridge. The term is applied to the two united lower petals of flowers of the pea family.

Lanceolate. Lance-shaped; broadest near the base and gradually tapering to the apex.

Leaflet. A single division of a compound leaf.

Linear. Long and narrow, with parallel margins.

Lobed. Divided into or bearing segments.

Midrib. The central vein of a leaf.

Node. The point of attachment of leaves and branches.

Oblong. Two or three times longer than broad and with nearly parallel sides.

Opposite. Referring to leaves inserted at the same level on both sides of the stem, or to flower parts inserted one directly in front of the other, as stamen opposite the petal.

Ovary. That part of the pistil which contains the ovules.

Ovate. Shaped like the longitudinal section of a hen's egg, the broader end basal.

Palmate. Spreading from a central point like the fingers of the hand.

Panicle. A pyramidal, loosely branched flower cluster, as in a compound raceme.

Pappus. The specialized calyx of members of the sunflower family; composed of bristles, scales, awns, or hairlike structures.

Perennial. A plant which lives and fruits year after year.

Peduncle. The stalk of a cluster of flowers.

Perianth. The floral envelopes, calyx or corolla, or both.

Persistent. Not falling off, remaining until the part which bears it is wholly matured, as the leaves of evergreens.

Petal. One of the divisions of the corolla.

Petiole. The support of a leaf.

Pinnate. Having the secondary veins or segments arranged along a midrib or rachis.

Raceme. A flower cluster in which the flowers are borne along the stem on individual stalks about equal in length.

Ray flower. One of the marginal flowers of a composite flower head.

Regular. The same all the way around, symmetrical in shape or structure.

Rootstock or Rhizome. An underground perennial stem.

Rosette. A cluster of crowded radiating leaves at the base of a stem.

Segment. One of the divisions into which a plant organ is cleft.

Sepal. One of the leaflike structures constituing the outer series of flower parts.

Serrate. Having sharp teeth pointing forward.

Sessile. Lacking a stalk.

Simple. In one piece, opposed to compound.

Spadix. A spike with a fleshy axis.

Spathe. A large bract enclosing a flower cluster, generally a spadix.

Spike. A flower cluster in which the blossoms are borne directly on the central stalk without individual flower stalks.

Stamen. The pollen-bearing organ of the flower, consisting of anther and filament.

Stipule. Appendages of the leaf borne in pairs at the base of the petiole.

Superior. Refers to an ovary which is borne above the attachment of the calyx.

Tendril. Threadlike portion of a plant which is used in climbing.

Trailing. Lying on the ground or over other plants, but not rooting at the nodes.

Two-lipped. Refers to an irregular calyx or corolla which has distinct upper and lower divisions.

Umbel. An inflorescence in which a cluster of flower stalks springs from the same point like the ribs of an umbrella.

Veins. Threads of conducting tissue in a leaf or flower part.

Venation. The vein arrangement.

Whorl. A group of leaves or other structures at a single node.

Abbreviations

Agh.	Carl A. Agardh
Ait.	William Aiton
Andr.	Henry C. Andrews
Applegate	Elmer Ivan Applegate
B. and H.	George Bentham and Joseph Dalton Hooker
Baker	John Gilbert Baker
Banks	Joseph Banks
Benth.	George Bentham
Bernh.	Johann Jacob Bernhardi
Betcke	Ernst Friedrich Betcke
Brew.	William H. Brewer
C. and S.	Adalbert von Chamisso and Diedrich Franz Leonhard von Schlechtendal
Cham.	Adalbert von Chamisso
Cogn.	Alfred Cogniaux
Cronq.	Arthur Cronquist
Cyrill.	Domenico Maria Leone Cirillo
DC.	Augustin Pyramus DeCandolle
Desf.	René Louiche Desfontaines
Donn	James Donn
Dougl.	David Douglas
Fisch.	Friedrich Ernst Ludwig von Fischer
Focke	Wilhelm Olbers Focke
Forbes	James Forbes
Fries	Elias Magnus Fries
Gmel.	Johann Georg Gmelin
Gray	Asa Gray
Gray, S. F.	Samuel Frederick Gray

Greene	Edward Lee Greene
H. and A.	William Jackson Hooker and George Arnold Walker Arnott
Heller	Amos Arthur Heller
Hoffm.	Georg Franz Hoffmann
Hook.	William Jackson Hooker
Howell	Thomas Howell
Hultén and St. John	Oskar Eric Hultén and Harold St. John
Jepson	Willis Linn Jepson
Johnst.	Ivan M. Johnston
Kostel.	Vincenz Franz Kosteletzky
Kuntze	Carl Ernst Otto Kuntze
L.	Carolus Linnaeus (Carl von Linné)
Ledeb.	Carl Friedrich von Ledebour
Less.	Christian Friedrich Lessing
L'Her.	Charles L'Heritier de Brutelle
Lindl.	John Lindley
Link	Johann Heinrich Friedrich Link
Maxim.	Karl Johann Maximowicz
Medic.	Friedrich Casimir Medicus
Michx.	André Michaux
Mill.	Phillip Miller
Morr. and Dcne.	Charles Jacques Edouard Morren and Joseph Decaisne
Muhl.	Gotthilf Henry Ernest Muhlenberg
Murr	Josef Murr
Nutt.	Thomas Nuttall
Oakes	William Oakes
Pers.	Christiaan Hendrik Persoon
Piper	Charles V. Piper
Poir.	Jean Louis Marie Poiret
Porter	Thomas Conrad Porter
Presl	Karel Boriwog Presl
Presl, J. and C.	Jan S. and Karel B. Presl
Pursh	Frederick Traugott Pursh
Raf.	Constantine Samuel Rafinesque-Schmaltz
Rehd.	Alfred Rehder
Roth	Albrecht Wilhelm Roth
Schwein	Lewis David de Schweinitz
Scop.	Johann Anton Scopoli
Sibth.	John Sibthorp
Sm.	James Edward Smith

Sm., C. P.	Charles Piper Smith
St. John	Harold St. John
Stev.	Christian Steven
Suksd.	Wilhelm Nikolaus Suksdorf
Sweet	Robert Sweet
T. and G.	John Torrey and Asa Gray
Torr.	John Torrey
Trel.	William Trelease
Wats.	Sereno Watson
Willd.	Carl L. Willdenow

Bibliography

Abrams, Leroy. *Illustrated Flora of the Pacific States*. Stanford University: Stanford University Press, 1940.

Alden, Roland H., and John D. Ifft. *Early Naturalists in the Far West*. (Occasional Papers of the California Academy of Sciences, No. 20.) San Francisco, 1943.

Bentham, G., and J. D. Hooker. *Handbook of the British Flora: A Description of the Flowering Plants and Ferns Indigenous to, or Naturalised in, the British Isles*. London: L. Reeve and Co., 1904.

Currants and Gooseberries and Their Culture and Relation to White-Pine Blister Rust. (United States Department of Agriculture Farmers' Bulletin, No. 1398.) Washington, D. C.

Dayton, W. A. *Important Western Browse Plants*. (United States Department of Agriculture Miscellaneous Publications, No. 101.) Washington, D. C., 1931.

Fernald, M. L. *Gray's Manual of Botany*. New York: American Book Co., 1950.

-------, and A. C. Kinsey. *Edible Wild Plants of Eastern North America*. Cornwall-on-Hudson, N. Y.: Idlewild Press, 1943.

Gilkey, Helen M., assisted by Garland M. Powell. *Handbook of Northwest Flowering Plants*. 2nd. ed. Portland, Ore.: Binfords and Mort, 1951.

Hardy, G. A. *Fifty Edible Plants in British Columbia*. (Handbook No. 1 of the British Columbia Provincial Museum, Victoria, B. C.) Victoria, B. C., 1942.

Haskin, L. L. *Wild Flowers of the Pacific Coast*. Portland, Ore.: Metropolitan Press, 1934.

Hutchinson, John. *Common Wild Flowers*. Middlesex: Penguin
Books, 1948

Jackson, Benjamin D. *A Glossary of Botanic Terms with Their
Derivation and Accent*. 4th ed., rev. and enl. Philadelphia:
J. B. Lippincott Co., 1928.

Jepson, W. L. *A Manual of the Flowering Plants of California*.
Berkeley: University of California Press, 1925.

Peck, M. E. *A Manual of the Higher Plants of Oregon*. Portland,
Ore.: Binfords and Mort, 1941.

Robbins, W. W., M. K. Bellue, and W. S. Ball. *Weeds of California*. Sacramento: State Department of Agriculture, 1941.

Sampson, Arthur W., and H. E. Malmsten. *Stock-poisoning Plants
of California.* (University of California Bulletin, No. 593.) Berkeley: University of California Press, 1935.

Saunders, C. F. *Western Wild Flowers and Their Stories*. Garden
City, N.Y.: Doubleday, Doran and Co., 1933.

Scullen, H. A., and G. A. Vansell. *Nectar and Pollen Plants of
Oregon*. (Oregon State Agricultural Experiment Station Bulletin,
No. 412.) Corvallis, Ore., 1942.

Stuhr, Ernst T. *Manual of Pacific Coast Drug Plants*. Lancaster,
Pa.: Science Press Printing Co., 1933.

Index

Numbers in italics refer to illustrations.